FURTHER GENERAL PROGRESS PAPERS

PUPILS' BOOK

WRITTEN BY H H THOMAS   REVISED BY A J THOMAS

Nelson

Preface

It was with great trepidation and humility that I approached the revision of this series, which has been continuously in print and used by children for thirty-five years, with sales exceeding ten million copies.

I have tried to preserve the spirit and flavour of the originals, while altering them to reflect the immense changes in our society in the intervening years. The series was intended to "teach by doing" rather than to serve only as test material. I have tried to continue that principle and to extend it.

I have received an enormous amount of help. Above all I am indebted to my wife, Myrna. Her help has been invaluable. In addition to contributing a large amount of the new material, she has been a constant source of inspiration and ideas. I am also indebted to my daughters, Lisa, Sarah and Mary, for many valuable suggestions, to my brother Dr. C.W. Thomas for his constructive criticism of the revised manuscripts, and to the many others who have helped me but are too numerous to name.

With so much help of quality, any failings in this revised series rest solely on my own inadequacy.   AJT

Notes to teachers and parents

1. This series of papers is designed to help measure the progress of children between the ages of 10 and 12 years. It also aims to *develop* their reasoning and problem-solving skills.
2. The very able pupil who has practised thoroughly might be expected to attain a high score when 45 minutes is allowed for a complete paper.
3. These papers should prove of equal value to the less able or less experienced pupil who can benefit greatly from practice and exposure to problem-solving. These children should be given much more time to deal with the questions and allowed to explore some of the questions at leisure. They should not be discouraged if they are slow to start with; speed will come with familiarity and understanding with practice. Even when the pupil cannot solve a particular problem after some time, he/she should be encouraged to look at the answer and then try to work out how it should have been done.
4. In marking, one mark is allowed for each answer and that answer is normally the standard answer in the Answer Book. It is inevitable, however, that an occasional question should have an alternative answer which is as valid as the one given. In this case discretion should be used. A lively debate about the validity of an answer is likely to teach a great deal.

Instructions to pupils

(i)   One mark is allowed for each answer.
(ii) Read each question most carefully to be sure that you fully understand it.
(iii) Pupils should learn to follow instructions precisely. Failure to do so frequently loses candidates many marks in school or public examinations. Note the following points in particular.

  a If asked to cross out certain words, the pupil should do so by drawing a single black line through the words and not cross out anything else.
  b If a pupil is asked to put a ring round a word or underline a word, this should be done and nothing else.
  c Sometimes the question requires that *one* word should be underlined, and sometimes *two* words. Care should be taken to do exactly what is asked.
  d Answers must be placed in the spaces allowed for them, not in the margin or any other odd space that happens to be there.

If these instructions seem to be rather fussy, remember that in school or public examinations, examiners have a very large number of papers to mark and they do not have the time to search for the answers or judge whether the candidate knew the right answer but wrote it incorrectly. *Get used to being precise and scoring all the marks of which you are capable.*

A.J.T.

1 What letter appears twice in the word **economy** but only once in the word **second**? ....

2 What letters appear in the word **second** and not in **economy**? ....

3 What letters appear in **economy** and not in **second**? ....

4 If there are more letters in **second** than there are in **economy** write **No**; if there are fewer write **Yes**. ....

[5–13]
In each of the following sets, if the two words have the same meaning underline the word **same**. If they are opposite in meaning, underline the word **opposite**. If they are neither, underline the word **neither**.

5	expand	enlarge	same	opposite	neither
6	scene	seen	same	opposite	neither
7	uncommon	rare	same	opposite	neither
8	bless	curse	same	opposite	neither
9	male	masculine	same	opposite	neither
10	artificial	natural	same	opposite	neither
11	mad	sane	same	opposite	neither
12	convenient	useful	same	opposite	neither
13	singular	plural	same	opposite	neither

[14–19]
Underline the word in brackets which fits with the three words on the left.

14 Monday Wednesday Friday (holiday, Saturday, February, Easter)

15 William Harry Timothy (Mandy, boy, girl, John)

16 daisy rose tulip (fern, grass, marigold, flower)

17 quarter half third (fraction, piece, tenth, second)

18 beautiful lovely pretty (ugly, complexion, handsome, plain)

19 hour second minute (time, day, noon, clock)

[20–27]
In these sentences the order of the words is confused. Find out what each would mean if arranged correctly. Then if it is true write **T**, or if it is not true write **F**.

Examples: **cows fly can** .... F

        can be eaten bread .... T

20   drink is good to water ....

21   school friends is to make the place ....

22   accidents cause careless drivers ....

23   quickly makes time go the hard work ....

24   day-time some in people sleep the ....

25   time clocks all correct keep ....

26   size the cows occasionally dogs are as same ....

27   accurate tired one when difficult is be to is it ....

[28–32]
Complete the following by underlining the appropriate word in the brackets:

28   **tiny** is to **enormous** as **minnow** is to (sea, shrimp, huge, eel, shark)

29   **fire** is to **conflagration** as **wind** is to (breeze, zephyr, gale, hurricane, storm)

30   **learning** is to **study** as **skill** is to (practice, trying, cleverness, dexterity)

31   **happiness** is to **sorrow** as **success** is to (grief, prize, tears, failure, victory)

32   **work** is to **pay** as **finding** is to (keeping, reward, satisfaction, losing)

[33–42]
In an antique shop the owner used a code so that the customers would not know the prices. In this code a table costing £548 was marked **NAI**, a clock which cost £196 was marked **BRD**, a picture costing £207 was marked **OLG** and a silver candlestick costing £135 was marked **BYN**. Find the code and encode the following prices:

33   £275   34   £369 ....

35   £438   36   £801 ....

What prices are the following?

37   **AGL**   38   **NDY** ....

Now try to complete the code table:

39–42	1	2	3	4	5	6	7	8	9	0
	....	....	....	....	....	....	....	....	....	

[43–47]

43 James is twice as old as his sister Rachel, but three years younger than his brother Michael. Michael will be 16 in three years time. How old is Rachel?

....

44 Mary is taller than Julia but shorter than Alice. Who is the tallest of the three?

....

45 Simon is bigger than Jason who is smaller than Bruce. Roger is bigger than Bruce but smaller than Simon. Who is the biggest?

....

46 Who comes next in size?

....

47 Who is the smallest?

....

[48–52]

Six women, Alice, Beth, Carole, Diana, Emily and Fiona, went to a sale. Alice and Emily both bought dresses, Beth and Fiona each bought a coat, Alice and Carole bought socks, Beth and Fiona bought berets, Carole and Emily each bought a shirt and Carole and Fiona bought gloves.

48 Who bought a dress and a shirt?

....

49 Who bought gloves and socks?

....

50 Who bought gloves and a coat?

....

51 Who bought a dress and socks?

....

52 Who bought nothing at the sale?

....

[53–57]

In each of the following lines, underline the word that means the opposite of the word on the left.

53 **abroad**   foreign   home   country   England   astray

54 **conceal**   hide   cover   lose   find   reveal

55 **stupid**   silly   ignorant   intelligent   dull   rude

56 **contract**   bargain   expand   desire   invent   lengthen

57 **modern**   elderly   new   fashionable   ancient   worker

[58–62]

In each of the following lines, underline the word that means the same as the word on the left.

58 **anger**   joy   sorrow   wrath   desire   hatred

59 **peaceful**   tempestuous   stormy   pleasant   calm   smooth

60 **empty**   full   vacant   engaged   roomy   airy

61 **lonely**   singular   peculiar   friendly   solitary   reticent

62 **powerful**   giant   tyrannical   cruel   weak   potent

[63–66]
James arrived on time for school. Tim came after him and Sue immediately before Tim. Helen was early, but Jane was last of all in getting to school.

63 Who arrived at school first? ....

64 Who arrived second? ....

65 Who came third? ....

66 How many were late? ....

67 Four times a certain number is three more than twenty-nine. What is the number? ....

[68–75]
Complete the following series by adding one item at the beginning and end of each line:

68–69 .... 9 12 15 18 21 ....

70–71 .... 42 37 33 30 28 ....

72–73 .... 234 345 456 567 678 ....

74–75 .... BD CE DF EG FH ....

[76–79]
Underline the correct word in the brackets.

76 **greater** is to **smaller** as **more** is to (least, greatest, lowest, lesser, less)

77 **far** is to **farther** as **good** is to (mother, better, best, farthest, goodness)

78 **right** is to **wrong** as **order** is to (chaos, untidiness, carelessness, neatness, weakness)

79 **up** is to **down** as **top** is to (centre, side, bottom, summit, edge)

[80–84]
Harriet was born five years before John. John is two years younger than William who is five years younger than Mary. William is five.

80 How old is Harriet? ....

81 Who is the eldest of the four children? ....

82 How old is Mary? ....

83 In how many years time will John be as old as Mary is now?

....

84 How much older than William is Harriet? ....

[85–94]

The following list shows how far these towns are from London:

Richmond	13 km	Birmingham	174 km
Guildford	45 km	Manchester	293 km
Maidstone	54 km	York	310 km
Oxford	87 km	Beaumaris	384 km
Cheltenham	155 km	Edinburgh	594 km

85 Which town is exactly twice as far from London as Oxford is?

....

86 How much farther is Manchester from London than Cheltenham is?

....

87 Which town is half as far from London as York is? ....

88 Which town is farthest of all from London? ....

89 How much farther from London is Manchester than Birmingham is?

....

90 If York is on the line between London and Edinburgh, how far is York from Edinburgh? ....

91 If the ordinary single fare is at the rate of 5p per km, how much should it cost to go from London to Birmingham? ....

92 To which of these towns should the single fare from London be £4.35?

....

93 How much more should the single fare from London to Oxford cost than the single fare from London to Maidstone? ....

94 What should the single fare from London to Edinburgh cost?

....

[95–100]

95–96 A non-stop coach leaves Liverpool for London on the motorway and travels at 80 km per hour. A return non-stop coach leaves Birmingham at the same time travelling at 75 km per hour. How far apart are the coaches one hour before they pass each other?

....

97–98 You are on holiday at the seaside. A yacht is anchored in the bay and has a rope ladder hanging over the side. The distance between each pair of rungs is 30 cm and there are 5 rungs. The bottom rung is just touching the water. The sea is calm and the tide is coming in so that the water level is rising at 20 cm per hour. How soon will the water cover the third rung of the ladder?

....

99–100 Six girls who are close friends take it in turns to bring sandwiches for lunch at school. It is Alison's turn and she has brought six neatly packed lunches in a basket. How can she divide the lunches so that each girl has one, yet one remains in the basket?

....

1 Cross out every word with fewer than four letters in this sentence:
In less than five days we shall have a holiday.

2 In this sentence part of a word is not wanted. Cross out the unwanted letters of that word to make the sentence correct:
The boy fell and broke his arm when they was sliding on the ice.

3–4 Fill in the missing figures in the following subtractions:

$$\begin{array}{r} 157 \\ .8 \\ \hline 79 \end{array} \qquad \begin{array}{r} 3.8 \\ 134 \\ \hline 184 \end{array}$$

[5–7]
Underline the correct answer in the brackets.

5 The numbers on the face of a clock add up to (66, 72, 78, 60, 84)

6 John was born in 1976 and James was born in 1971 so James is (twice as old as John, half as old as John, 5 years older than John, the same age as John, 5 years younger than John).

7 I bought two ice creams at 33p each and so had (13p, 27p, 36p, 34p, 33p) change from a £1 coin.

8 If a man is older than his son put a cross in a square unless he is also older than his daughter in which case write the word **No**. ....

9 Put the right answers to the questions in the spaces:

Three sheep have .... legs.   One sheep has .... legs.

[10–18]
In each of the following sets, if the first two words have a similar meaning underline the word **same**. If they are opposite in meaning underline the word **opposite** and if they are neither underline the word **neither**.

10	hot	warm	same	opposite	neither
11	freezing	boiling	same	opposite	neither
12	fire	heat	same	opposite	neither
13	hearth	stove	same	opposite	neither
14	trivial	petty	same	opposite	neither
15	friend	enemy	same	opposite	neither
16	desire	need	same	opposite	neither
17	wealthy	happy	same	opposite	neither
18	rich	satisfied	same	opposite	neither

[19–28]
In each of the following lines there is one word which does not fit in with the rest. Cross it out.

19	cat	pig	elephant	trout	horse	rat
20	coal	spinach	iron	copper	gold	oil
21	Spain	Italy	Peru	Belgium	Holland	Denmark
22	run	jump	leap	sprint	climb	sleep
23	house	flat	bungalow	stable	cottage	mansion
24	bottle	jug	knife	kettle	teapot	jar
25	Paris	Rome	Amsterdam	Bristol	Madrid	Athens
26	robin	thrush	sparrow	starling	parrot	blue-tit
27	Germany	Europe	Africa	Asia	America	
28	flea	frog	fly	ant	wasp	beetle

[29–35]
Underline the greatest, and ring the least of the following:

29	elephant	mouse	cat	dog	horse	rat
30	crowd	congregation	multitude	group	gathering	
31	several	some	many	couple	thousands	scores
32	1.02 kg	1200 g	2.01 kg	2100 g	0.864 kg	
33	0.70 cm	0.07 cm	6 cm	8 mm	74 mm	
34	villa	bungalow	palace	cottage	hut	house
35	1325	3125	2135	5123	1235	15023

[36–42]
Fill in the appropriate word or number to complete the following:

36 **cork** is to **float** as **lead** is to ....

37 **gas** is to **pipe** as **electricity** is to ....

38 **March** is to **month** as **autumn** is to ....

39 **January** is to **December** as **first** is to ....

40 **spring** is to **youth** as **winter** is to ....

41 **12** is to **18** as **40** is to ....

42 **50** is to **10** as **100** is to ....

[43–45]
Fill in the answers:

43 If 2 is subtracted from 3 times a certain number the answer is 25.

What is the number? ....

44 Twice **a** is equal to 6 times 5. What is **a**? ....

45 Half of **z** is 2.5 times 8. What is **z**? ....

[46–51]
A shopkeeper uses the word **NEIGHBOUR** as a code word to mark the prices of his goods. Thus **N** = 1, **E** = 2, **I** = 3, etc. and **N.GB** would stand for £1.46. Decode the purchase prices of the articles marked:

46 **G.OU** ....   47 **I.NN** ....   48 **ERG** ....

49 How would £3.85 be coded? ....

50 Give the code for £4.93. ....

51 What code would he use for £27.50? ....

[52–57]
Look at the words given below. If a word contains both **a** and **e** put **1** in the space, if **a** but not **e**, put **2**, if **e** but not **a** put **3**, if neither **a** nor **e** put **4**; if **e** or **a** comes twice put **5**.

52 cease ....   53 cart ....   54 certain ....

55 sure ....   56 curious ....   57 tether ....

[58–67]
Here is a passage in which one word on each line has become jumbled. Put the corrected word in the space at the end of the line.

58 Physical tivicaty will help you to stay slim ....

59 and axler your body. It will keep you full of ....

60 vitality, give tone to your cumless and, for ....

61 older people, will elph to keep them feeling ....

62 younger for longer. Good tinage and sleeping ....

63 habits and antsleap attitudes to other people will ....

64 all help to keep you fit for file. Fresh air ....

65 and glusthin are especially important for health. ....

66 Heyhalt people do not need medicines, drugs and ....

67 battles to keep them well. They need exercise. ....

[68–71]
Underline the two words in each line which make another word when spelled backwards.

68–69 lain   lair   nail   lade   dale   rail   dial   load

70–71 team   tame   mate   meat   meet   mite   item   emit

[72–76]
There are five men on a building site, Alec, Bill, Colin, Dave and Ted. Alec, Bill and Colin together weigh less than Dave, Alec and Bill. Alec, Colin and Dave together weigh more than Alec, Bill and Dave. Alec and Ted are the heaviest pair, while Ted is the lightest.

72–76 Put them in descending order of weight.

1 ....   2 ....   3 ....   4 ....   5 ....

[77–80]
Cross out the one word which does not fit in with the others. Put a ring around the general word which includes those which remain.

77–78 I   you   person   it   she   he

79–80 slipper   laces   trainer   shoe   sandal   footwear

[81–85]
There is a family of four children. Susan was born 5 years before David. David is four years older than Richard and 3 years younger than Tim. Susan is seventeen.

81 Who is the eldest?   ....

82 How old is Richard?   ....

83 How much older is Tim than Richard?   ....

84 In how many years' time will Richard be as old as Tim is now?

    ....

85 In how many years' time will Susan be twice as old as Richard?

    ....

[86–89]
Complete the following series:

86   1   10   19   28   37   ....

87 200   190   175   155   130   ....

88   3   20   37   20   3   20   ....

89 A1   C3   E5   G7   I9   ....

[90–100]

Would you make a good detective?

Five children went on a nature study walk with their teacher. Their names were Lucy, Julian, David, Tina and Rachel. When they returned to the classroom the teacher opened her handbag to get the keys for her desk and was startled by a frog leaping out. As the handbag was closed she could not believe that the frog had got into the bag by accident and assumed that one of the children must have put it there as a practical joke. She had been very startled and she questioned all the children.

These are their statements:

Lucy: (1) I didn't put it there. (2) I have never played a practical joke. (3) Tina did it.

Julian: (4) I didn't put the frog there. (5) I like frogs and am kind to them. (6) Rachel knows who did it.

David: (7) I didn't touch any frogs. (8) I didn't see Rachel do anything, but I wasn't near her most of the time. (9) Tina did it.

Tina: (10) I am not guilty. (11) Rachel did it. (12) Lucy was lying when she said I did it.

Rachel: (13) I didn't touch the teacher's handbag. (14) Julian did it. (15) David knows I didn't do it because he was with me all the time.

These statements did not help to find the culprit, so when the children had been kept after school for an hour they admitted that they had each told one lie but insisted that their other statements were true. Which were the true statements? Fill in the numbers.

90–91 Tina ___10___ and ___11___   92–93 David ___7___ and ___8___

94–95 Rachel ___13___ and ___14___   96–97 Lucy ___1___ and ___2___

98–99 Julian ___5___ and ___6___

100 Who committed the awful crime? _____

1 Which letter occurs most often in the word **appropriate**?

....

2 Which letter occurs twice in **appropriate** and once in **province**?

....

3 Which letters occur once in **province** and not at all in **appropriate**?

....

[4–8]

4 Take the next even number greater than 8 from the next odd number smaller than 15. Write the answer. ....

5 What is the middle number between 13 and 19? ....

6 If 13 is greater than 11 put a square in a circle unless 13 is also less than 14, in which case write the word **Yes**. ....

7 Take the smallest odd number from the largest even number:

7 3 6 9 5 ⑧ ① 3 ....

8 I bought 5 18p stamps and gave a £1 coin. If my change was more than 10p write the word **Yes**. Otherwise write **No**. ....

[9–14]

Give the opposites of the following words. They all begin with **f**.

9 past .... 10 strange ....

11 success .... 12 sensible ....

13 unbreakable .... 14 enemy ....

[15–19]

Underline the correct word in the brackets.

15 **come** is to **go** as **win** is to (loose, fail, lose, gain, prize)

16 **question** is to **answer** as **query** is to (correct, knowledge, ignorance, response, decision)

17 **clever** is to **cleverness** as **dangerous** is to (dangerously, safely, safety, danger, carelessness)

18 **friend** is to **enemy** as **beauty** is to (beast, loveliness, ugly, hideous, ugliness)

19 **hand** is to **finger** as **foot** is to (ankle, heel, toe, bone, nail)

[20–24]

There is one number wrong in each of the following series. Cross it out and write the correct number in the space provided.

20   1   4   7   10   14   16   19   ....

21   3   6   9   12   15   19   21   ....

22   4   9   16   25   36   48   64   ....

23   96   84   75   60   48   36   24   ....

24 160   80   40   30   10   5   2.5   ....

[25–33]

Here is a target in a shooting gallery. 10 points are given when a shot hits the bull's eye, 6 points for any shot within the next circle, 4 for any within the next, and 2 for any in the outer circle. Each person has five shots. No points are awarded if the target is missed.

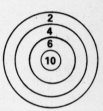

25   What is the highest number of points which can be scored? ....

26   What is the lowest number of points which can be scored? ....

27   What is the lowest number of points which can be scored with every shot

hitting th፥ target? ....

Here are the cards of 5 competitors showing their hits on the target.

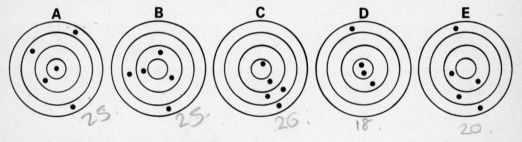

28   Which scored the most points? ....

29   Which had the lowest score? ....

30   Which missed the target with some shots? ....

31   Which two competitors had the same score? ....

32   Which two together scored as many as **D** and **E** together?

....

33   How many more points did the winner score than the person who came

second? ....

[34–38]
Cross out the unwanted parts of these sentences.

34 The man took his what off the peg.

35 The old man limping up the road was a windower.

36 The farmer was ploughing the island to prepare for planting his outcrops.

37 Shall we go know?

38 The best manager lost the hearing just before the wedding.

[39–43]
Underline the two sets of figures in each line that give the same answer:

39	4×4	8×3	$36/9$	6×6	$32/2$
40	$15/3$	2×9	7×5	$8 + 4 + 6$	$36/3$
41	$4 + 9 + 3$	8×3	$24/2$	$28 - 12$	$13 + 6$
42	$19 - 5$	7×4	$49/7$	$29 - 15$	$8 + 9$
43	$23 + 1$	4×7	$36/2$	$7 + 13 + 4$	9×3

[44–52]
Underline what should come first and last, or the largest and smallest in the following sets:

44	foundations	walls	chimneys	roof	plan	house
45	thrush	duck	starling	wren	blackbird	pigeon
46	35 mins	110 mins	1 hr 12 mins	¾ hr	105 secs	1¼ hrs
47	yacht	tugboat	trawler	canoe	tanker	
48	minnow	trout	herring	shark	tadpole	salmon
49	3000 m	2.6 km	865 m	0.793 m	2.060 km	
50	1953	5391	9531	1593	1359	3591
51	£0.75	54p	£1.01	£0.50	110p	
52	23 Mar	30 Jan	4 July	18 Nov	9 May	20 Jan

[53–57]
Underline the two words, one in each set of brackets, which go together in a way similar to the first two words:

53 **kilometre** is to **length** as (litre, gram, Celsius) is to (hour, time, weight)

54 **mother** is to **child** as (horse, cow, mare) is to (pup, stallion, foal)

55 **good** is to **best** as (better, little, late) is to (best, least, later)

56 **tall** is to **taller** as (bad, good, little) is to (best, worse, worst)

57 **lion** is to **lioness** as (fox, badger, stag) is to (ram, ewe, vixen)

[58–64]

In each of the following lines there is one word which still makes a sensible word if spelled backwards. Underline it.

58   male   lame   laid   meat   ream   mare

59   voter   store   week   meet   steer   weird

60   real   seal   said   liar   dear   weed

61   mead   maid   dame   shed   read   raps

62   never   matter   silver   lever   slaver   defer

63   team   tame   mate   mire   moor   late

64   part   stag   stir   trip   plot   rapt

[65–68]

Underline the correct answer:

65   A ship always has (sails, a propeller, an engine, a funnel, a rudder)

66   A house always has (tenants, furniture, drains, television, doors)

67   Which of these has no legs, but can move fast and lives on land? (snail, hare, worm, tortoise, eel, fish, snake)

68   Which of these is a bird, but cannot fly or swim? (puffin, penguin, dodo, eagle, ostrich, pheasant)

[69–78]

Underline the two words on each line that are most alike in some way but different from the rest.

69   green   yellow   pink   velvet   blue   silk

70   lawyer   surgeon   teacher   doctor   vicar   plumber

71   Snowdon   Wales   Thames   London   County   Severn

72   spoiled   evil   fine   rotten   wicked   good

73   snake   sparrow   butterfly   elephant   eagle   nest

74   lovely   beautiful   ugly   rich   happy   poor

75   friend   enemy   partner   companion   ally   foe

76   chicken   rabbit   duck   goose   squirrel   pheasant

77   happy   brave   rich   cowardly   bright   wealthy

78   skill   safety   danger   wisdom   care   peril

[79–86]

Four passengers were sitting in a compartment in a train travelling from Manchester to Glasgow. One was from Liverpool, another from Oldham, a third from Warrington, and the last was from Chester. Their names were Andrews, Barnes, Cadbury and Dutton.

Mr. Andrews and the woman from Chester were doctors.

Mrs. Dutton and the man from Oldham were teachers.

The person from Liverpool is older than Mrs. Dutton.

The person from Chester is fair and Mrs. Dutton is dark.

At Carlisle, Mr. Barnes and the man from Liverpool left the train.

79   Mrs. Dutton is from   ....

80   Mrs. Cadbury is from   ....

81   Mr. Andrews is from   ....

82   Mr. Barnes is from   ....

83–84   The two teachers are .... and ....

85–86   The two doctors are .... and ....

[87–96]

In each of the lines in the following passage there is one word with the letters mixed up. Find the word, underline it and then write it correctly in the space provided.

87   Some resay ago a terrible blizzard swept   ....

88   over Britain, burying the country endur   ....

89   deep snow. Traffic saw   ....

90   brought to a standstill and many malls   ....

91   villages were completely desolati from the   ....

92   outside world. Thousands of peshe perished   ....

93   in the snow in tipse of the efforts of   ....

94   the shepherds who loited day and night   ....

95   to extricate the poor serrutace from the   ....

96   deep drifts which evcrode the ground.   ....

[97–100]

These are some questions to test how well you can follow instructions.

97 Turn to Paper 1 in this book. What is the second word of question 48?

....

98 In Paper 1, question 67, what is the seventh word? ....

99 Again Paper 1, question 67; what is the product of the seventh word and the first word? ....

100 Turn to Paper 2, question 25. If the capital of Spain is mentioned put a circle in a square, unless the capital of France is also there, in which case put a cross in a circle. ....

[1–10]

1 Which letter occurs most often in the longest word of the following sentence:

Everbody admires the perseverance of the scholar. ....

2 Draw a ring around the fifth letter of the sixth word in the following sentence:

I was very lucky in finding the door already open.

3–4 In this sentence one word is missing. Put a cross (x) where the missing word should be and write the word in the space provided.

Autumn is the of mists and mellow fruitfulness. ....

5 Write the letter **m** twice between the second and first vowels in the alphabet.

....

6–7 Arrange these words in the spaces, putting together the things that are alike:

silver   slippers   steel   shoes

.... and .... go together.

.... and .... go together.

8 Fill in the missing figure in the following sum:

7)37.2
  536

9 Underline the word in brackets which makes the best sentence.

If you want to (exceed, secede, succeed, recede) you must work hard.

10 In four years' time I shall be three times as old as Mary who is now nine.

How old am I? ....

[11–13]
Read the following and answer the questions by underlining the correct word in the brackets.

Julie runs faster than Brian but not as fast as Susie, who is slower than Andrew.

11 Who is the fastest runner? (Brian, Susie, Julie, Andrew)

12 Who is the slowest runner? (Brian, Susie, Julie, Andrew)

13 Who would come second in a race between them?
(Brian, Susie, Julie, Andrew)

[14–21]
Underline the first and last or the greatest and least in each line:

14 father   child   grandfather   son   baby   daughter

15 mouse   cat   horse   rat   goat   rabbit

16 trawler   liner   schooner   frigate   tugboat   canoe

17 crowd   gang   couple   throng   multitude   mob

18 pea   bean   potato   marrow   leek

19 1866   6816   6618   8618   8661   1668

20 1 June   31 Oct   17 Nov   8 April   31 March

21 10 mm   5 cm   22 ft   22 m   100 yds   100 m

[22–28]
In each of the following lines, underline the two things which are most alike and yet different from the rest:

22 peach   oak   ash   elm   plum   birch

23 beef   veal   trout   sole   lamb   pork

24 tea   beer   cocoa   milk   cider   water

25 greed   patience   kindness   honesty   envy   love

26 billiards   snooker   cricket   football   tennis   hockey

27 rose   salvia   daisy   petunia   crocus   buttercup

28 pekinese   persian   burmese   tabby   poodle   siamese

[29–35]
Linda has a younger sister called Ruth, a brother Paul who is older than she is, and a cousin Diana whose brother George is the youngest of all.

29 How many sisters has Paul?   ....

30 Who is Paul's female cousin?   ....

31 Who is Diana's male cousin?   ....

32 Who is the youngest child in Linda's family?   ....

33 Who is the eldest child in Linda's family?   ....

34 Who is George's sister?   ....

35 Who is Paul's youngest sister?   ....

[36–40]
Underline the word which best describes the word in heavy type.

36 A **beech** is a kind of (seashore, apple, tree, flower)

37 A **pair** is a (couple, fruit, flower, bird, blossom)

38 A **tale** is a (part of an animal, story, book, monkey)

39 To **question** means to (resist, shout, discuss, inquire, argue)

40 To **comprehend** means to (believe, explain, understand, find, know)

[41–50]
Here is a group of children training
to be a marching group, for the school
festival. They are facing the wall.
The instructor is on the spot marked *,
on a line from **L** to **O**.

WALL _____ *Instructor

D	R	G	O
N	F	C	P
T	U	V	A
L	M	X	Z

41 How many children are in the group? ....

Underline the correct answers in brackets. If they all turned to face right:

42 Which would be in the front row? (**D, T, R, P, X, Z**)

43 Which one would be immediately behind **V**? (**X, C, A, U, M, F**)

44 Which would be in the back row? (**O, Z, D, R, M, L**)

45 Which one would be directly in front of **F**? (**N, R, U, C**)

If, instead of turning to face right, they had turned to face left:

46 Which would be in the front row? (**D, M, R, P, T, Z**)

47 Which would be directly in front of **X**? (**Z, U, M, V**)

48 Which would be in the third row? (**U, M, C, F, Z**)

If they turned to face the instructor:

49 Who would be farthest away from the instructor? ....

50 Who would now be behind **P**? ....

[51–54]
In the school sports, because 10-year-old boys vary a lot in size, they
decided to run the fourth year running race as a handicap. David gave
John 10 seconds and Ian 6 seconds start. John won the race from Ian by 2
seconds with David third, 9 seconds behind.
Underline the right answer:

51 Is John slower than David?   Yes   No   I cannot tell

52 Who is the fastest?   John   Ian   David

53 How much longer than Ian did John take? 1 sec   2 secs   same time

54 Who is the slowest of the three?   John   Ian   David

55 I bought some books on Tuesday, I bought three times as many on Wednesday and five more on Thursday. Altogether I bought seventeen books. How many did I buy on Tuesday? ....

[56–60]
In a code, **xrhomtvr** stands for the word **straight**. Underline the correct answer in the brackets.

56 What must **vmtv** stand for? (tart, sits, high, hits)

57 What is the word coded by **xmtvr**? (tarts, right, sight, high)

58 **rvor** codes for (hat, hits, that, rats)

59 What does **xrohx** stand for? (stirs, start, stars, grass, rats)

60 What is the code for **thirst**? ....

[61–74]
My parents and I are selecting a holiday from a travel brochure. To help us choose we have made a list of the particular features we want for our holiday:

(a) A beautiful setting   (b) Quiet sandy beaches
(c) A harbour with fishing boats   (d) Windsurfing
(e) Plenty of night-life with discos, a pier with entertainments and a theatre

Looking through the brochure, we find a number of resorts in the area we want to go to. They are:

Redcliffe: a large town with theatres, discos, two piers, a shingle beach, a swimming pool, a harbour with boats for hire and a fair.

Sand Bay: a tiny fishing village with long sandy beaches, a little harbour with fishing boats, and a little pier.

Southpool: a busy small resort with a public swimming pool, cinemas, a theatre on the pier, a sandy beach with water sports, and discos at night.

Westmouth: a small resort set in a large wooded cove. There is a small fishing harbour adjoining a sweeping sandy beach with various water sports. It is lively at night with discos, theatre and a cinema and outdoor entertainment. There is no swimming pool.

Eastmouth: a fairly small fishing village with a pier, a harbour and fishing from a shingle beach. There are cliffs to climb and small rocky islands off the beach. At night the village becomes alive with open-air theatre, discos and street entertainment.

61–70 Which place best meets our needs for our holiday? ....

71–72 If we could not find suitable accommodation at our first choice which should we choose? ....

73–74 If we had to go to our second choice what should we miss?

....

[75–78]
Underline the word in each set of brackets which most suitably completes the line:

75   **hand** is to **arm** as (foot, toe, ankle) is to (wrist, heel, leg)

76   **feathers** are to **birds** as **scales** are to (grasshoppers, eels, fish, frogs, hedgehogs)

77   **boo** is to **jeer** as (shout, hiss, cheer) is to (discourage, criticise, applaud)

78   **time** is to **watch** as (heat, temperature, cold) is to (degrees, oven, thermometer)

[79–84]
Underline the correct answer in the brackets.

79   Are girls sometimes stronger than boys? (Yes, No)

80   Are criminals always caught? (Yes, No)

81   Are conceited people sometimes clever? (Yes, No)

82   Does a candidate always do himself justice in an examination? (Yes, No)

83   Are summers in Britain always hot? (Yes, No)

84   Are all television programmes interesting to watch? (Yes, No)

[85–93]
To drive off in a car you have to get in and start the engine, after making sure the door is closed and fastening your seat belt. You start the engine by putting in the key and turning it. Then you select first gear, after pressing down the clutch. Slowly release the clutch after checking in your rear view mirror that there is nothing coming behind, and drive off. Don't forget to release the handbrake.

Write a checklist for a learner driver, putting the instructions in the strict order in which you would have to do them. One instruction per line.

Get in the car.

85   ....

86   ....

87   ....

88   ....

89   ....

90   ....

91   ....

92   ....

93   ....

[94–100]

Here is a tried and tested recipe for making marmalade.

I wish to make a larger batch than the recipe provides for and I have large enough vessels in which to do it. I propose to make half as much again and I have left spaces in the recipe for the changed amounts. Fill in the changes that I need to make.

Seville Orange Marmalade

1 .... kg Seville oranges   2 .... kg sugar

1 .... litre water   Juice of 2 .... lemons

Wash the oranges and remove the peel and pips. Cut up the fruit roughly and shred peel according to taste. Tie the pips in a muslin bag. Put the cut up fruit, peel, pips and water in a pressure cooker and cook for 10

.... minutes. Reduce pressure at room temperature, remove bag of pips and add warmed sugar and strained lemon juice. Stir until sugar is dissolved. Boil in a large open pan until the setting point is reached

(approx. 7 .... minutes).

Yield — approx. 6 .... kg.

[1–5]
Underline the correct answer in the brackets.

1 I am 9 years older than Tim who was born on 10th January 1973. I was therefore born in (1980, 1985, 1964, 1954, 1895).

2 David had 24p more than I had, and I had 17p. David therefore had (31p, 44p, 7p, 41p, 34p).

3 I bought three 18p stamps and four 13p stamps. I therefore had (24p, 16p, 48p, 44p, 4p) change from £1.50.

4 John can walk at 6 kilometres an hour. John can therefore walk one kilometre in (5, 10, 15, 20, 25) minutes.

5 I am Mr. Bramwell's niece. He is therefore my (aunt, cousin, father, uncle).

[6–10]
Complete each of these series by filling in the spaces:

6	3	6	12	24	48	....
7	3	8	14	19	25	....
8	....	48	36	24	....	
9	7350	735	73·5	7·35	....	....
10	½	¾	⅚	⅞	....	....

[11–15]
Cross out the odd word in each line:

11	Julian	John	Stephen	Diana	Brian	Martin
12	aunt	friend	cousin	nephew	uncle	father
13	cabbage	cauliflower	broccoli	sprouts	tomato	
14	Spain	Belgium	France	U.S.A.	Japan	Peking
15	brush	pencil	pen	chalk	crayon	easel

[16–20]
Here are some mixed up occupations. Can you sort them out? Fill in the correct word in the space provided.

16 You might ask a **lickybarre** to build you a wall. ....

17 A **mestich** will provide a remedy for a cough. ....

18 If your T.V. breaks down call the **geenrein**. ....

19 Your first caller in the morning will probably be the **mopstan**. ....

20 If not it will be the **pabyrope** or the **prilgrape**. ....

[21–25]
Underline the two words, one in each set of brackets, which go together in a similar way to the words in heavy type.

21 **cricket** is to **ball** as (badminton, hockey, rugby) is to (racquet, shuttlecock, players)

22 **pond** is to **fish** as (town, lake, sea) is to (houses, animals, people)

23 **fifth** is to **tenth** as (fourth, seventh, third) is to (eleventh, eighth, thirteenth)

24 **penny** is to **pound** as (millimetre, centimetre, metre) is to (kilometre, millimetre, metre)

25 **sight** is to **eyes** as (taste, smell, feel) is to (hear, touch, nose)

[26–31]
Anna, Lisa, Erin, Sara and Melissa are five girls. Anna, Sara and Melissa are short. The rest are tall. Lisa, Sara and Melissa are dark; the others are fair. Lisa, Erin and Melissa have long curly hair; the other two wear their straight hair short.
In the classroom:

26 In the front desk sits ...., a short girl with dark curly hair.

27 Behind her sits ...., a tall girl with fair curly hair.

28 On her right is ...., who is tall with dark curly hair.

29 On her left sits ...., a short girl with dark short straight hair.

30–31 The remaining girl is .... and she is ....

....

[32–43]
In a code the following numbers represent the words below them but not necessarily in that order:

7213   9273   638   72456   728138   725638

her   fame   faith   father   safe   farmer

Code the following words:

32 master ....   33 same ....   34 feet ....

35 steamer ....   36 farther ....   37 trash ....

Decode the following numbers:

38 729538 ....   39 8321 ....   40 8493 ....

41 74895 ....   42 56313 ....   43 1325 ....

[44–55]

The following list shows the cost of single scheduled air fares to various places in Europe from London (Heathrow):

Athens	£240	Oslo	£116
Cyprus	£300	Moscow	£245
Copenhagen	£82	Nice	£106
Frankfurt	£66	Paris	£33
Gibraltar	£173	Rome	£183
Istanbul	£245	Stockholm	£160

If the fares are priced at a standard rate per km:

44 What place is the same distance from London as Moscow is?

45 Which destination is the farthest from London?

46 Which city is the nearest to London?

47 Which city is just over half as far from London as Cyprus is?

48 Which Scandinavian city is about half as far from London as Stockholm is?

49 Rome is almost the same distance from London as .... and .... combined.

50 If Paris is on the direct route to Nice, how much would you expect to pay to travel from Paris to Nice?

51 If the budget return fare to Cyprus was £450, what would be the budget return fare to Athens?

52 How much would it cost to travel from Stockholm to Gibraltar via London?

If Athens is 2400 km from London:

53 How much farther is it to Istanbul than to Athens?

54 How far is it to Oslo?

55 What distance is the journey from Moscow to Nice, stopping at London on the way?

[56–63]
Underline the correct word in the brackets:

56 **loud** is to **shout** as **quiet** is to (silent, whisper, talk, whistle, scream)

57 **water** is to **liquid** as **ice** is to (ice cream, water, fluid, solid, crack)

58 **tree** is to **roots** as **house** is to (roof, foundations, walls, drains, site)

59 **people** are to **village** as **rabbits** are to (burrow, den, warren, field)

60 **today** is to **tomorrow** as **yesterday** is to (tomorrow, Tuesday, today, past, future)

61 **42** is to **24** as **64** is to (48, 84, 46, 23, 128)

62 **18** is to **54** as **12** is to (108, 18, 96, 42, 36)

63 **57** is to **19** as **48** is to (21, 20, 16, 46, 47, 49, 42)

[64–67]
If $a = 5$, $b = 4$, $c = 3$, $d = 7$ and $e = 2$, give the numerical values of:

64 $\dfrac{b \times d}{e} = $ ....

65 $a + b + c - e = $ ....

66 $\dfrac{a \times b \times c}{e} = $ ....

67 $(c + d + e) \times b = $ ....

What three letters added together will make the numbers in brackets?

68 (10) ....

69 (11) ....

70 (14) ....

71 How many millimetres are there in $b \times c \times e$ centimetres? ....

72 How many weeks are there in $b \times c \times d$ days? ....

73 How many minutes are there in $a \times b \times c \times e$ seconds? ....

[74–78]
In each of the following, underline the two words in the brackets that give the correct answer:

74 Tin is always a (vegetable, can, mineral, vessel, utensil, metal)

75 Tigers are always (old, striped, tame, animals, captive, gentle)

76 Amsterdam is a (city, village, river, mountain, port)

77 In Britain clothes are (essential, unnecessary, cheap, useful, wasteful)

78 Coaches always have (wheels, passengers, punctures, tyres, horses, accidents, drivers)

[79–88]
Alec, Bruce, Clive, Donald and Edward are five men who want to get together to play golf in the evening.
Alec is free on Tuesday, Wednesday and Saturday evenings.

Bruce is working late on Wednesdays and Thursdays. He is also away all day on Sundays.
Clive has Monday and Saturday evenings free.
Donald cannot play on Monday, Thursday, Friday or Sunday evenings.
Edward can play on any evening except Tuesday and Sunday.

79 Which day can they all play? ....

80 When can none of them play? ....

81 Which day are the smallest number free? ....

82 When, except Saturday, can Alec play with Edward? ....

83 When, except Saturday, can Bruce play with Clive? ....

84 When, except Saturday, can Bruce play with Donald? ....

85 Can Bruce, Clive and Edward play together on any day other than

Saturday? ....

86 Who can play together on Wednesdays? ....

87 Who can play together on Thursdays? ....

88 Who can play on the least number of days? ....

[89–100]
In the passage below a word has been left out of each line. The place where it should go is marked with a cross (x). Choose the word from the list and write it in the space at the end of the line.

89 County shows have long x the "shop window" ....

90 of the agricultural x, showing both town and ....

91 country the types of x and crops which the ....

92 farmers x. There are competitions for the best ....

93 livestock of each kind as well as x for working dogs ....

94 and exhibitions of x farm machinery. Traditionally ....

95 the county show provided a grand outing for the x ....

96 farming community x neighbouring country folk could ....

97 meet, exchange gossip, x animals and buy goods. ....

98 Above all it was a great x occasion. Unfortunately, in ....

99 recent years, costs have x and attendances have fallen ....

100 so that the x Agricultural Show has become all too rare. ....

produce   animals   been   modern   community   shows

where   county   social   barter   scattered   risen

[1–3]

1 What letter appears twice in **destination** but only once in **dictation**?

....

2 What letter appears only once in the word **level**? ....

3 What letter appears once in **destination** and twice in **departure**?

....

[4–8]
Underline the word or phrase in the brackets which gives the best answer to each question:

4 I am eighty years of age. Therefore I am (a young man, an old soldier, a middle-aged woman, an old man).

5 I visited my mother's brother. He is my (step-father, uncle, aunt, grandfather, son).

6 I saw a man painting the windows of a house. He was a (carpenter, plumber, mason, decorator).

7 I had severe stomach pains, so my mother sent for the (butcher, chemist, chiropodist, doctor, undertaker).

8 I bought six 13p stamps and gave eight 10p pieces in payment, so I had (4p, 12p, 2p, 22p, 8p) in change.

[9–16]
Underline the correct word in the brackets:

9 **soot** is to **black** as **snow** is to (ice, cold, water, white, blue)

10 **fox** is to **cub** as **hare** is to (pup, cub, bunny, leveret, young)

11 **fox** is to **vixen** as **rabbit** is to (hind, doe, fawn, buck, squirrel)

12 **bird** is to **air** as **fish** is to (ocean, water, scales, net, basket)

13 **bear** is to **fur** as **sheep** is to (fleece, skin, grass, lamb, ewe, wool)

14 **good** is to **reward** as **bad** is to (prison, sentence, naughty, temper, punishment)

15 **here** is to **where** as **now** is to (place, when, time, age, present)

16 **hot** is to **cold** as **riches** is to (wealth, poverty, plenty, fortune, scarcity)

Underline the correct answer in the brackets:

17 I bought 1 kg of apples. I gave my brother Jonathan two apples, each weighing 70g, and my sister Mary three, each weighing 95g. I therefore had (500g, 425g, 575g, 475g, 525g) left.

[18–21]
William is learning a part for a play. This is a description of the character he will portray:
He has many friends and rarely quarrels with any of them. He shares his toys and sweets and always has a smile for everyone. Although his parents are poor and he has few clothes, he is always neat and clean.
From the words below, select four which best describe the character. Underline them.

gregarious   **quarrelsome**   **spiteful**   **mean**   **happy**

rich   **generous**   **selfish**   **careless**   **careful**

[22–27]
Here are some more mixed up words. Find the word and write it in the space.

22   A clock has a laid and so does a radio.   ....

23   A toast is a small wild animal found in Britain.   ....

24   Gropride is a breakfast food originally from Scotland.   ....

25   Sameles is fortunately becoming a rare disease.   ....

26   A home would be very uncomfortable without craish.   ....

27   Most schools have a yorundgalp.   ....

[28–35]
Look at this diagram. It has five rows, **1, 2, 3, 4** and **5**.
There are letters in each of these rows: e.g. the letters in row **1** are **E N T E R**.
It also has five columns marked **I, II, III, IV** and **V** in Roman numerals. There are also letters in each column: e.g. the letters in column **IV** are **E L P E D**.

	I	II	III	IV	V
1	E	N	T	E	R
2	V	I	O	L	A
3	E	C	O	P	S
4	N	E	V	E	R
5	T	R	A	D	E

Now answer the questions:

28   One letter **V** is in line 2, column **I**.

The other **V** is in line ...., column ....

29   Which letter occurs most frequently in the squares?   ....

30   Which letter is in line 3, column **IV**?   ....

31   How many columns form recognisable words?   ....

32   Which line does not form a word?   ....

33   Which column does not contain the letter **E**?   ....

34   What is the position of the letter **D**? Line .... Column ....

35   How many words can you recognise altogether?   ....

[36–45]

The following numbers are in code for the words below them, but not in the same order.

23641   325541   3254   5236   1264

pact   capped   acted   date   cape

Decode the following numbers:

36 23641 ....

37 325541 ....

38 5236 ....

39 3254 ....

40 1264 ....

41 5234 ....

42 642 ....

Code the following words:

43 tact ....

44 petted ....

45 peace ....

[46–52]

Fill in the missing figures in these examples:

46–48
$$\begin{array}{r} \ldots \\ 635 \\ \hline 296 \\ \hline \end{array} -$$

49–50
$$\begin{array}{r} 4. \\ 35 \\ 46 \\ \hline 13. \\ \hline \end{array} +$$

51– 52
$$\begin{array}{r} 7. \\ 8 \\ \hline 6.2 \\ \hline \end{array} \times$$

[53–58]

Underline the correct answer in the brackets:

53 **boxer** is to **ring** as **actor** is to (arena, circus, stage, footlights, scene)

54 **bird** is to **nest** as **rabbit** is to (burrow, field, fur, den)

55 **hunger** is to **eat** as **thirst** is to (water, drink, dry, tea, supper)

56 **right** is to **wrong** as **transparent** is to (invisible, thick, opaque, thin, brittle)

57 **eighteen** is to **ten** as **nine** is to (twenty-seven, twenty, thirty, five, thirty-six)

58 **12** is to **18** as **18** is to (9, 24, 27, 36, 6)

[59–63]

For the following, $a = 3$, $b = 4$, $c = 5$, $d = 8$, $e = 9$.

59 Divide **e** by **a** and give the answer as a letter. ....

60 Divide **(a + e)** by **b**. Give the numerical answer. ....

61 **(a + d + e)** divided by **c** gives which letter? ....

62 What number must be added to **d** to equal **c + e**? ....

63 What is the numerical value of $\dfrac{(a \times d)}{(b + d)}$? ....

[64–72]

Look at the following words. If the letters **n** and **i** occur in a word, put **1** on the dotted line. If **n** but not **i** occurs, put **2**. If **i** but not **n** occurs, put **3**. If neither **n** nor **i** occurs put **4**, and if either **n** or **i** occurs more than once in a word put **5**.

64 clean .... **65** certain .... **66** climbed ....

67 clamber .... **68** train .... **69** difficulty ....

70 brain .... **71** cannon .... **72** pigeon ....

[73–83]

Here is a family tree. The sign = means "married" and the downstrokes signify "children of".

Mr. and Mrs. F. Wilkinson

Jane = Frank Hyde   Mary = James Robins   Tom = Florence Grey

Mary William Tom   Alice Richard   Sally Henry Julia Helen

73 How many grandchildren have Mr. and Mrs. Wilkinson?

....

74 How many children have Mr. and Mrs. Robins? ....

75 How many grandchildren bear the surname Wilkinson? ....

76 What relation is Frank Hyde to Florence Grey? ....

77 What relation is Alice to Jane? ....

78 What is Jane's married name? ....

79 What is Florence's married name? ....

80 What relation is Richard to Sally? ....

81 What relation is Tom Hyde to Mr. F. Wilkinson? ....

82 How many people are now called Wilkinson? ....

83 How many are there in the Hyde family? ....

[84–100]

This is a treasure hunt. You are given a map of a piece of common land. Somewhere on this land treasure has been buried, and there are clues chalked on stones or on walls in various places to help you find it. Follow the instructions to travel the route that you must take to pick up all the clues. Collect the clues and write them in the order that you pass them.

From the start walk 50 paces to the west, then 30 paces north and 30 paces east. Proceed to the ruined farm buildings to the north-west, crossing the bridge. Walk up the hill to the north-east until you reach a small shepherd's hut near the top. From there walk towards the start for 40 paces and cross the bridge. Take 20 paces in the direction of the most northerly tall tree and then turn due south for another 40 paces. Finally walk 75 paces in a south-south-easterly direction. You should now have all the clues.

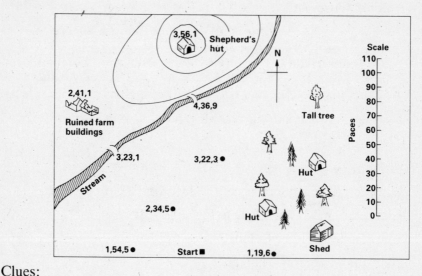

Clues:

84	....	85	....	86	....	87	....
88	....	89	....	90	....	91	....

All these clues have three numbers: the first number refers to a Paper in this book; the second number refers to a question in that Paper. The third number refers to a word or number in that question: e.g. 4,56,6 means the sixth word (or number) of question 56 in Paper 4 of this book.

These clues make up the instructions to find the treasure. Look up the clues and complete the instructions.

92–100   .... the .... It is .... paces north-east from the start. .... paces west is a .... Walk .... paces along its shadow at .... Here lies the treasure. Mark it on the map with a cross (x).

[1–6]

Look at these words and then answer the following questions.

facetious friendship theatre troubles dialogue

1   Which is the longest word?   ....

2   Which is the shortest word?   ....

3   Which two words have most letters the same?   ....

                                                                    and ....

4   What letter occurs in the word **dialogue** and in none of the others?

                                                                    ....

5   Which letter occurs most frequently?   ....

6   Which letter occurs in **facetious** and in none of the others?

                                                                    ....

[7–11]

Underline the correct word in the brackets.

7   **speech** is to **hearing** as **dumb** is to (sound, sight, hearing, deaf, blind)

8   **ear** is to **hearing** as **mouth** is to (sound, speech, tongue, sight, nose)

9   **actor** is to **audience** as **preacher** is to (congregation, crowd, pulpit, reader, print)

10   **speech** is to **speaker** as **picture** is to (audience, artist, viewer, fans, academy)

11   **speech** is to **sight** as **dumb** is to (deaf, hearing, blind, colour, talking)

[12–15]

12   I was standing in the sun and my shadow was to the west. I turned around and faced the opposite way. In what direction did my shadow now point?

                                                                    ....

13   When I was walking to school early this morning my shadow was on my right-hand side. What direction was the school from my house?

                                                                    ....

14   On my way home from school in the late afternoon, which side should my shadow be?   ....

15   A car was travelling at 60 km per hour over a bridge 250 m long. How many seconds would it take to cross the bridge?   ....

[16–21]
In the diagram, put one letter in each small square so that each line makes a word. Each word should include **A R** in the positions in which you find them. A clue is given to help you.

16 The opposite of **departure**.

17 A house on wheels.

18 One who pleases greatly.

19 Gives out information.

20 You do this to find points of likeness.

21 A Russian tea urn.

A	R					
	A	R				
		A	R			
			A	R		
				A	R	
					A	R

[22–27]
In each of the sets, underline the word which is different from the others:

22 motorway road   avenue   street   villa   footpath

23 silk   dress   cotton   satin   muslin   nylon

24 day   week   second   month   first   year

25 cake   bead   tart   pie   bread   loaf

26 wind   rain   sleet   winter   snow   hail

27 saucepan   wine glass   tumbler   beaker   mug   tankard

[28–36]
Here is the key to a code. The alphabet is shifted by two letters to the left.

a b c d e f g h i j k l m n o p q r s t u v w x y z
C D E F G H I J K L M N O P Q R S T U V W X Y Z A B
Underline the decoded word in the brackets.

28 **DQA** stands for (**toy, cow, boy, coy, bow**).

29 **NWOR** stands for (**lamp, limp, limb, lump, lane**).

30 **Bird** would be coded as (**DLUF, DKTF, BKQG, CLTE, DKIF**).

31 **Knife** would be coded as (**NPKDC, MPJGE, NQKHE, MPKIG, MPKHG**).

32 Which day of the week would be coded as **VWGUFCA**? ....

33 Which month of the year would occur as **HGDTWCTA** in the code?

....

34 Give the code word for **Saturday**. ....

35 Give the code for **November**. ....

36 What is the code for **autumn**? ....

[37–41]
In each of the sets below, underline the word that means the opposite of the first word:

37	**attract** draw	repel	befriend	like	dislike
38	**positive** absolute	real	unreal	negative	indirect
39	**cause** origin	source	end	aim	effect
40	**cherish** help	keep	abandon	hate	lose
41	**convict** prison	wickedness	innocence	acquit	guilt

[42–46]
Here are some sentences which do not make sense but would if you interchanged two words. Underline the two words you would interchange.

42 The wet has been really weather.

43 It is often night at dark.

44 Many children enjoy their school at work.

45 Winter always comes before autumn.

46 The son was much older than his father.

[47–50]
Underline the word in the brackets which correctly completes the sentence.

47 **England** is to **London** as the **United States** is to (France, New York, Chicago, Washington D.C., Scotland)

48 **head** is to **hat** as **foot** is to (brush, sole, shoe, leather, polish)

49 **wash** is to **clean** as **stain** is to (rinse, moisten, iron, dirty, destroy)

50 **sight** is to **telescope** as **speech** is to (audience, telegram, letter, microphone)

[51–55]
John is twenty. Two years ago he was three times as old as his sister Kate who is five years younger than her brother Neil.

51 How old is Kate now? ....

52 How old is Neil? ....

53 How much older is John than Neil? ....

54 What age was John when Kate was born? ....

55 How old will John be when Kate is as old as he is now? ....

[56–58]

56 What time is three-quarters of an hour later than 1045 hours?

....

57 If it is 0720 hours now, what time was it three-quarters of an hour ago?

....

58 If January 3rd is on a Monday, what day of the week will January 28th be?

....

[59–60]
Underline the correct answer:

59 My train leaves at 1810 hours. My watch is 6 minutes fast. I arrive at the platform of the station at 1804 by my watch. (I have missed my train by 4 minutes, I am just in time, I have 4 minutes to wait, I have 12 minutes to wait)

60 My watch is 8 minutes slow and my train normally goes at 1845 but is 5 minutes late. I get to the station at 1845 by my watch. (I am just in time, I miss the train, I have to wait 13 minutes, I have to wait 3 minutes)

[61–65]
In each of the sets, underline the three things which are alike:

61 elm   beach   fur   oak   ash   bin   wood

62 music   piano   songbook   violin   singing   cello   choir

63 paper   ceiling   brush   magazine   book   wall   paint

64 spaniel   otter   badger   terrier   eel   salmon   alsatian

65 parcel   string   package   cord   blind   rope   stamp

[66–71]
Alex, Charles and Eve are three British athletes who meet up with some others at the European Games. Boris and Herman speak German; Alex and Herman speak French; Boris and Eve speak Spanish; and Charles speaks Russian.

66 Who can converse in either English or Spanish?   ....

67 Who can speak English or French?   ....

68 Who can speak German and French?   ....

69 Could Alex and Herman carry on a conversation?   ....

70 Could Herman and Eve understand each other?   ....

71 Could Alex, Boris and Herman converse with each other?

....

[72–76]

In each of the first five lines of this passage there is a word which is wrong and which makes the passage silly. Underline the word that is wrong and write the correct word in the space.

72 The sun was setting in the east as Tim   ....

73 James and his brother William Hill set   ....

74 out one morning to visit her aunt.   ....

75 He lived in a picturesque cottage in the country   ....

76 and her name was Mrs. Hepplethwaite for she had

married Tim's father's brother.   ....

[77–82]

O===O===O===O===O===O===O===O
A   **Z**

Here are eight stations on a suburban railway line. We shall call them **A, E, D, R, O, I, M** and **Z**. A train goes back and forth between **A** and **Z** several times a day, but it does not stop at all the stations every time. On one trip from **A** to **Z** it stops at **M, I** and **D** successively. Coming back it stops at **E, D, O** and **M** in that order. On the next trip from **A** to **Z** it calls at **R, M, D** and **E** before reaching **Z**, and returning it stops at **D**, then **I**, then **O**, then **M** before reaching **A**.

Write the stations in their proper order.

A .... **Z**

[83–86]
Underline the word in the brackets which goes best with the first three words.

83 sorrow   grief   misery   (joy, anger, happiness, sadness, hatred)

84 play   recreation   amusement   (work, labour, fun, interest)

85 help   aid   succour   (hinder, watch, assist, check, renew)

86 quick   sharp   hurried   (funny, speedy, clever, cunning, slow)

[87–96]

Here are three rows of children gathered in the playground and facing their teacher whose position is marked by an (*). Behind them is a wall.

_____ **Wall**

A D G J M

B E H K N

C F I L O

*

Teacher

87 Which two children are farthest away from their teacher?

....

88 Which child is nearest to the teacher?   ....

If they all turn to face left:

89 Who will be immediately behind **H**?   ....

90 Which of these will now be in the back row? (**E, D, M, B, F**)

....

91 Which will then be in the front row? (**F, D, M, A, C**) ....

92 Who will now be nearest the teacher? ....

If they all turn left again:

93 Which of these are now in the back row? (**D, J, B, M, C, O**)

....

94 Who is now immediately in front of **K**? ....

95 Who is immediately behind **E**? ....

96 Underline the instruction in brackets, that the teacher would now need to give to make the class face her: (right turn, left turn, about turn, nothing at all).

[97–100]

Cross out words or parts of words to make this sentence sensible.

97–100 The judge dismissed the injury because several of them were suffering from threat crash and were quite still.

[1–5]

1 Fill in the word which best completes this sentence:

I walk faster than James; therefore James walks more .... than I do.

2 Cross out all the odd numbers less than 9 in the following:

1 12 13 3 11 14 5 6 7 9 10 8 15

3 Cross out the unwanted word:

The infant child was nearly twelve years of age.

4 Cross out the unwanted part of a word:

The youngest child was over seventy years old.

5 Helen's birthday is on Christmas Day. Tina is five days younger than Helen. If Christmas Day falls on a Friday, on which day is Tina's birthday?

....

[6–12]

Underline the word in the brackets which gives the correct answer:

6 **road** is to **car** as **canal** is to (canoe, ship, traffic, barge, lock)

7 **cottage** is to **thatch** as **house** is to (walls, tiles, ceiling, chimney, bricks)

8 **Z** is to **A** as **death** is to (life, baby, childhood, birth, grave)

9 **cricket** is to **bat** as **snooker** is to (table, chalk, cue, pocket, balls)

10 **leg** is to **knee** as **door** is to (hinge, lock, key, well)

11 **fat** is to **thin** as **nourish** is to (feed, starve, eat, drink, thrive)

12 **hot** is to **temperature** as **heavy** is to (steam, weight, wet, cold)

[13–18]

Five people go shopping on the same bus to the town. They are John, Steven, Julie, Sue, and Carol.

Julie buys shoes; Carol and Sue buy groceries; Carol also buys two dresses. Steven buys socks; Julie, Carol and Steven also buy soap. At the last minute, John and Steven pick up some fruit and Carol and Sue buy some cakes.

13   Who buys both groceries and cakes? ....

14   Who has both soap and fruit? ....

15   Who has soap and cakes? ....

16   Who has shoes and soap? ....

17   Who buys the least number of things? ....

18   Who has been to the most shops? ....

[19–24]

In each of the following sets, underline the word that means the same as the word on the left.

19	**intention**	question	purpose	argument	answer	idea
20	**quake**	old-fashioned	fear	squeal	tremble	disrupt
21	**glare**	brightness	dazzle	annoy	gleam	stare
22	**meddle**	interfere ·	reward	award	punish	strength
23	**timid**	quiet	small	noisy	shy	brave
24	**admit**	encourage	allow	confess	deny	enter

[25–28]

Complete the series by filling in the blanks.

25	....	D	G	J	M	....
26	....	R	O	L	I	....
27	....	YB	XC	WD	VE	....
28	....	Rq	Po	Nm	Lk	....

[29–50]

You have a friend in another country who is writing letters to you to try to improve her English, but she is just as keen to teach you some of her language too. She starts off by writing a letter in English with the phrases or sentences repeated in her language in brackets.

Dear Lucy,

I am pleased to write to you (**mea pleso scripti vu**) and I hope you will write back to me (**mea spero vu scripti mea**). I live in a house (**mea viva gan ront**). I live with my mother (**mea viva ut smere**). My mother stays in the house with my baby brother (**mi smere loco gan ront ut mi brerino**). My big brother works in the town (**mi largo brere laboro gan urbos**). I work hard in the school to write English (**mea laboro dura gan scola scripti Engliso**).

What do these mean:

29–32 **Mea pleso vu viva gan ront** ....

33–36 **Mea spero vu laboro gan scola** ....

37–40 **Mea spero vu viva ut smere ut brerino ut brere** ....

....

41–44 **Mea pleso vu scripti mea** ....

45–50 Translate this sentence into her language:

My mother is pleased you work hard in school to write English.

....

[51–55]
Underline the two words in the brackets which go together in a similar way to the words in heavy type.

51 **man** is to **talk** as (cat, horse, bark, squeal, neigh)

52 **sing** is to **opera** as (act, play, film, perform, theatre)

53 **buy** is to **sell** as (give, borrow, purchase, lend, present)

54 **sheep** is to **fold** as (bird, rabbit, weasel, den, burrow)

55 **driver** is to **car** as (conductor, violin, orchestra, concerto, ticket)

[56–60]
In each of the following sets, underline the word that is opposite in meaning to the word on the left.

56	**entrance**	door	exit	corridor	porch	outside
57	**latest**	least	last	original	earliest	first
58	**plenty**	enough	little	sufficient	rare	scarcity
59	**heroism**	bravery	reward	cowardice	frightened	savagery
60	**busy**	working	drone	laborious	employed	idle

[61–63]

If the months of the year came in the opposite order, beginning with December:

61 What would become the eighth month of the year? ....

62 What would be the fifth letter of the fifth month? ....

63 Which number would the month with the longest name become?

....

[64–73]

In each of the following, underline the word which includes all the others and ring the word which does not fit with the rest:

64–65 creature horse frog bird hill fly

66–67 plane tool screw chisel pliers hammer

68–69 minnow snake trout salmon perch fish

70–71 Bath Surrey county Cornwall Devon Essex

72–73 sapphire diamond ruby pearl emerald gemstone

[74–77]

Underline the two words in each of these lines that are alike in some way, but different from the rest:

74 villa stable kennel cowshed cottage sty

75 theatre museum cinema library town hall art gallery

76 pencil paper paint easel eraser brush

77 mean solitary happy joyful cruel brash

[78–83]

Here is a code. In it the words are represented by the numbers given, but not in that order.

meet **eats** **seat** **teas** **teem**

3162 2163 1623 2115 5112

Fill in the answers.

78 meet .... **79** seat .... **80** 2163 ....

81 5112 .... **82** team .... **83** steam ....

[84–86]

84 Which letter occurs three times in the word **advertisement** and twice in the word **separate**? ....

85 Which letter occurs twice in **separate** and once in **advertisement**?

....

86 Which letter occurs once in **separate** and twice in **advertisement**?

....

[87–91]
Here is a board divided into nine squares. The top three squares — **a, b** and **c** — are painted white. The middle row of squares — **d, e** and **f** — are painted red and the remaining squares are painted blue.
Now a second coat of paint is applied, but this time the left-hand column — **a, d** and **g** — is painted red. The middle column is painted white and the right-hand column is painted blue.
Thus the squares appear in different colours, e.g. white and red will give pink; blue and red will give purple. Which squares will be:

a	b	c
d	e	f
g	h	i

87 pale blue? .... **88** pink? ....

89 red? .... **90** purple? ....

91 white? ....

[92–94]
Underline the correct answer in the brackets.

92 **truth** is to **lie** as **teach** is to (help, mislead, annoy, hinder, educate)

93 **answer** is to **sum** as **solution** is to (detective, sugar, work, problem)

94 **pork** is to **pig** as **veal** is to (cow, lamb, sheep, calf, ox)

[95–100]
Place the letters in the squares according to the instructions. Read them carefully.

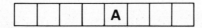

			A			

95 **M** is as far as possible from **A** but not next to **T**.

96 **Z** is between **A** and **T**.

97 **X** and **T** are at the ends.

98 **P** is next to **Z** but not next to **A**.

99 **R** is between **M** and **A**.

100 **V** is three squares from **X**.

[1–8]

1	2	3	4	5	6	7	8	9	10	11	12	13	14	15	16	17	18	19	20	21	22	23	24	25	26
a	b	c	d	e	f	g	h	i	j	k	l	m	n	o	p	q	r	s	t	u	v	w	x	y	z

We have numbered the alphabet for you to make these questions easier.

1 What is the 24th letter of the alphabet? ....

2 Which number is the letter **q**? ....

3 Give the numbers of the letters of the word **tank**. ....

4 What is the total of the numbers of the letters of **pit**? ....

5 Find the value of $\dfrac{j \times f}{c}$ ....

6 Find the value of $\dfrac{y \times d}{t}$ ....

7 Look at the word **exercise**. Find the letter which occurs most often in the word, find its value, and multiply this by the number of times the letter appears. Take the answer from the value of the letter in the word which is

nearest to the end of the alphabet. ....

8 What letter occurs once in the word **exercise** and three times in the word

extraordinary? ....

[9–13]

Words are arranged in a dictionary in strict alphabetical order. In each of the following lines indicate the first and last in that order by putting the letter **F** for "first" and **L** for "last" in the brackets next to the appropriate word.

9 beauty (   ) beast (   ) but (   ) bent (   ) bat (   )

10 clean (   ) clan (   ) clip (   ) clog (   ) claw (   )

11 danger (   ) drain (   ) dingy (   ) duke (   ) dame (   )

12 thought (   ) that (   ) there (   ) their (   ) this (   )

13 weight (   ) will (   ) worm (   ) went (   ) what (   )

[14–18]
Underline the correct word in the brackets.

14 **paper** is to **pencil** as **canvas** is to (easel, brush, paint, ruler, cotton)

15 **elephant** is to **trunk** as **bird** is to (beak, feathers, tail, wings, feet)

16 **air** is to **aeroplane** as **sea** is to (fish, shark, sailor, submarine, pearl)

17 **figures** are to **arithmetic** as **letters** are to (writing, postmen, geometry, dictionary, replies)

18 **illness** is to **treatment** as **poison** is to (drugs, death, antidote, pain, relief)

[19–23]
I have a small cube of cake 4 cm long on each side. The cake is brown and it is covered with pink icing.

19 I want to cut this block of cake into eight smaller cubes. How many cuts must I make? ....

20 What will be the length of each side of one of the smaller cubes?

....

21 How many sides of each of the smaller blocks will be covered with pink icing? ....

22 How many sides of each will show the brown cake? ....

23 I have a plank of wood 5 metres long. I want to cut it into lengths each a metre long. How many cuts will I have to make? ....

[24–31]
Let **a** = 2, **b** = 3, **c** = 5, **d** = 6, **e** = 8.

24 Give the letter which answers **b** × **a**. ....

25 $\dfrac{e \times b}{d}$ = (as a number) .... **26** **c** **c** = (as a letter) ....

27 Which two letters added together will give 9? ....

28 Which two letters multiplied together will give 18? ....

29 Which two letters multiplied together will equal **d**? ....

30 Which three letters added together will produce 17? ....

31 Which three letters added together and divided by **a** will equal **c**?

....

[32–41]

In each of the following lines, cross out the two words that fit least with the others:

32 cloudy   misty   sunny   rainy   foggy   clear

33 snow   frost   warmth   cold   ice   sunshine

34 alligator   crocodile   herring   lizard   turtle   shark

35 saucepan   potatoes   frying pan kettle   bottle   casserole

36 caterpillar snail   butterfly   grub   worm   bee

37 trumpet   conductor   orchestra   violin   cello   trombone

38 camel   yak   donkey   lion   horse   giraffe

39 table   chair   stool   bookcase   picture   sofa

40 lake   reservoir   pool   river   stream   pond

41 sheet   blanket   bed   pillow   duvet   quilt

[42–46]

Underline the correct answer in each of the following:

42 If a kettle containing a litre of water takes 4 minutes to boil, then the same kettle containing 2 litres of water should take (2 minutes, 8 minutes, the same time) to boil.

43 If a man can run 100 metres in 10 seconds, then two men should each run 100 metres in (5 seconds, 20 seconds, the same time).

44 If a man with a tractor can plough a field in one day, then two men with similar tractors should plough the field in (two days, the same time, half a day).

45 If it costs £300 to buy a television set for two people, then one for four people should cost (£600, £150, £75, the same amount).

46 If it takes four minutes to boil an egg in a saucepan, then it will take (8 minutes, 2 minutes, the same time) to boil two eggs in the same pan.

[47–50]

Underline the correct word in each pair of brackets.

47 **up** is to **down** as (wall, door, ceiling) is to (windows, floor, roof)

48 **goose** is to **geese** as (gander, lady, horse) is to (mare, lady's, ladies)

49 **valley** is to **vale** as (mountain, river, lake) is to (town, peak, hill)

50 **crowd** is to **people** as (swarm, shoal, herd) is to (spectators, insects, birds)

[51–55]

Underline the word which best shows the meaning of the word in heavy type.

51 To **raze** means to (lift, grow, destroy, build, shave)

52 A **beach** is a (flower, tree, seashore, shrub, insect)

53 **Frail** means (unsuccessful, sweet-smelling, difficult, old, fragile)

54 **Fare** means (food, light, beautiful, medium, just)

55 **Taut** means (learned, showed, mocked, tight, demonstrated)

[56–65]
Here is a histogram or bar graph which
shows the weights of a number of different
girls in a class. Read carefully the
information given and add the labels to
the graph. 2 marks for each label.

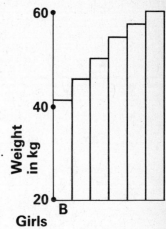

A, **B** and **D** are together heavier than **A**, **B** and **E**.
A, D and **E** are together lighter than **A, F** and **E**.
D, E and **F** are together lighter than **D, E** and **C**.
A and **B** are together lighter than **A** and **E**.
A is heavier than **B**, but lighter than **E**.

[66–70]
Linda is 5 years older than Lisa, who is three years younger than Jackie
who was born in 1977. They were all born in March.

Underline the correct answer in the brackets.

66 When was Lisa born? (1974, 1979, 1980, 1908)

67 In what year was Linda born? (1969, 1975, 1979, 1985)

68 How old will Linda be in 1990? (12, 13, 15, 22, 17)

69 If they have an elder brother Julian, who is 7 years older than Jackie, how
much older is he than Lisa? (4, 5, 8, 10, 12, 15) years

70 In what year was Julian born? (1960, 1965, 1970, 1972, 1975)

[71–74]
Underline the general word that includes all the others:

71 silk   satin   material   nylon   linen   cotton

72 relation   uncle   aunt   cousin   sister   father

73 steel   iron   tin   zinc   metal   gold

74 knight   earl   baronet   viscount   baron   rank

[75–86]
Here is a passage in which one word on each line is mixed up. Put the
correctly spelled word in the space at the end of the line.

75 Even very early man needed some kind of helster, ...

76 and just as dromen man is glad to reach home ....

77 after binge out in the wind and the rain, ...

78 our ometer ancestors sought shelter by making ....

79 windbreaks with woven branches and eslave. ....

80 Early man newdread far in search of food but gradually ....

81 he began to build terbet shelters. Some used caves ....

82 while others made crude ushoes in trees which they ....

83 reached with rope addlers. Other people became lake ....

84 redwells and made their houses by driving piles ....

85 into the bed of the leak and building houses on ....

86 flamsport above the water. They travelled by boat. ....

[87–93]
Look at the diagram and then answer the questions:

87 Which number is in the circle but not in a triangle or a square? ....

88 Which number is in a
square only? ....

89 Which number is in a circle and a
square only? ....

90 Which number is in a triangle, a
square and a circle? ....

91 What is the sum of the numbers in
the circle? ....

92 Which number is in a triangle only? ....

93 What is the sum of the numbers in
the triangle? ....

[94–100]
Alexandra had invited seven other children to
her party. They were Bruce, Serge, Nicola,
Emily, Frances, George and Helen. They were
to be seated at a round table and Alex had
already sat down. When the others came to sit
down Serge wanted to sit between Frances and
Helen. Nicola wanted to sit next to Bruce but
not next to George or Emily. Emily wanted to sit
next to Alex and opposite to Frances. Helen
wanted to sit next to Alex on her left side. Can
you place all the children round the table so that
everyone is satisfied?

Alexandra

1   Cross out every word beginning with **sh** in the following sentence:

Shall we see three ships sheltering in the harbour?

2   Part of this sentence is not needed. Cross it out.

Every Tuesday I go to town once a week.

3   Cross out the unwanted word:

The big giant had a small son

4   Cross out the unwanted parts of words in this sentence:

He was every unlucky to finding the treasure.

5–6   Put together the things that are alike:

plant   tree   climb   ascend

.... and .... go together.

.... and .... go together.

7–8   Underline sums with the correct answers:

$4 \div 12 = 48$ $9 \times 8 = 72$ $24 \times 6 = 4$ $3 \div 11 = 33$

$64 + 12 = 76$ $8 + 7 = 56$

9   How many legs has a horse? Write nothing but the answer.

A horse eats .... A horse has .... legs.

A cow has .... horns. A cow gives ....

10   If 8 is larger than 7 put a cross in a circle, unless 12 is larger than 13 in which case put a circle in a square.   ....

[11–17]
Underline the word which has an opposite meaning to the word on the left.

11 **remember**	celebrate	enjoy	forget	lost	ignore
12 **major**	miner	colonel	private	less	minor
13 **juvenile**	man	boy	child	adult	woman
14 **ancestor**	forefather	descendant	successor	predecessor	child
15 **private**	publish	known	famous	public	unknown
16 **health**	hospital	patient	operation	disease	nurse
17 **barren**	bare	wild	fertile	jungle	sparse

[18–22]
Underline the correct word in each set of brackets.

18 **book** is to **author** as (statue, statute, picture) is to (publisher, sculptor, reader)

19 **castle** is to **tower** as (church, farm, cottage) is to (window, spire, barn)

20 **sheep** is to **flock** as (cow, fish, bird) is to (gaggle, number, shoal)

21 **seldom** is to **often** as (many, scarce, rare) is to (ample, plentiful, none)

22 **clumsy** is to **graceful** as (heavy, awkward, polite) is to (foolish, rude, dull)

[23–31]
In shops such as antique shops, jewellers and second-hand stores the prices are not always fixed. In these shops codes are often used to mark the suggested pricing of the goods. Here is such a code. A ring valued at £58 would be marked **NB**, and ear-rings worth £6.75 marked **G.EN**. A bracelet worth £12.34 would be marked **ST.RA** and beads, value £9.00, would carry **O.XX** on the ticket. If this code is used, how would the price tickets be marked for goods worth the following amounts?

23 £3.10 ....

24 £4.09 ....

25 £37.50 ....

26 £745 ....

What would be the value of goods marked as follows?

27 **N.EG** ....

28 **TS.** ....

29 **.TN** ....

30 **.OO** ....

31 Now complete the code word:

   1   2   3   4   5   6   7   8   9   0

....

[32–36]
Underline the word that is similar in meaning to the word on the left.

32	**eccentric**	rare	fine	strange	quiet	humorous
33	**stubborn**	unco-operative	odd	obstinate	nasty	rude
34	**tiredness**	laziness	sadness	nonsense	excuse	fatigue
35	**angry**	eager	sad	fierce	irate	quiet
36	**forgiveness**	apology	pardon	friendship	love	amend

[37–39]
Cross out the odd word on each line:

37 man   woman   children   girl   adult   boy

38 uncle   aunt   father   nephew   son   grandfather

39 herd   flock   crowd   troop   pack   stage

[40–41]
Look at the following well-known proverbs. There are two which are nearly opposite in meaning. Put an **O** for "opposite" in the first column alongside them. There are also two which mean almost the same. Put **S** for "same" alongside the two proverbs, in the second column.

Look before you leap.   ....

A miss is as good as a mile.   ....

Discretion is the better part of valour.   ....

Faint heart never won fair lady.   ....

[42–45]
In this group of words there are three which do not fit in with the others. Cross them out. There is also a general word which includes all the others. Put a ring around it.

roar   bang   wolf   howl   zoo   cage

noise   rattle   shout   shriek   squeal   yell

[46–48]
Give the opposites of the words in heavy type:

46 A **difficult** problem ....

47 A **dull** game ....

48 A **stormy** night ....

[49–53]
Underline the correct word in the brackets.

49 **Sacred** means (scratched, secular, frightened, marked, holy).

50 A **melody** is a (musical instrument, player, tune, fruit).

51 A **bough** is (bending low, an instrument for shooting arrows, a branch, a tie, mistletoe).

52 **Copious** means (fine, plentiful, able to manage, too much, copying).

53 A **porpoise** is (an intention, a mammal, a reptile, something deliberate, a fruit, a fish).

[54–62]
Here is a street plan. Study it and then answer the questions.

C = Church
T = Town Hall
A = Art Gallery
M = Museum
RS = Railway Station
S = School
L = Library

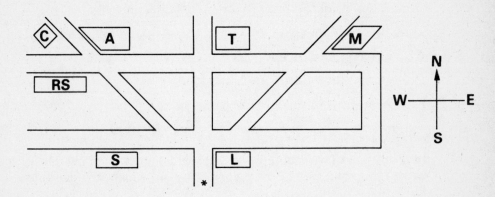

Suppose you are at the point marked * and looking up the street.

54 In which direction are you looking? ....

55 Which building is due south of the Town Hall? ....

56 Which building is due north of the School? ....

57 Which buildings are north-west of the School? ....

58 In which direction is the Library from the Museum? ....

59 If you take the second turning to your right and then the first left, which building will be on your right? ....

60 In which direction must you walk from the Railway Station to get to the Museum? ....

61 Starting from the School I walk east and then north-east. If I keep walking straight on, which building will I come to? ....

62 From the point marked * I walk up the street and take the first right. I walk on and take the second left and later on the next left turn.

Immediately on my right I see the ....

[63–66]

Angela, Rebecca, Colin, David and Susan count their money. Altogether they have £9. The girls together have twice as much as the boys.

63 How much have the girls together?   ....

Rebecca has as much as Angela and Susan together. Colin has the same amount as David. Angela has 50p more than David.

64 How much has Angela?   ....   **65**   How much has Colin?   ....

66 How much has Rebecca?   ....

[67–71]

Underline the correct word in the brackets:

67 **acting** is to **singing** as **play** is to (opera, theatre, music, television, recitation)

68 **leather** is to **boot** as **wool** is to (sheep, foot, shoe, sweater, loom)

69 **England** is to **country** as **Somerset** is to (parish, town, county, village, district)

70 **rabbit** is to **burrow** as **lion** is to (lair, den, cage, zoo, jungle)

71 **foolishness** is to **wisdom** as **danger** is to (carelessness, result, accident, death, safety)

[72–78]

72–78 The numbers **1, 2, 3, 4, 5, 6, 7, 8** and **9** need to be put into the squares in their proper places according to the following directions.

3, 7, 8 are in the top row.
2, 1, 9 are in the bottom row.
3, 9, 2, 6, 5, 8 are not in the
left-hand column.
7, 3, 6, 1, 4, 9 are not in the
right-hand column.

[79–84]

Here are some nonsense sentences, but they would mean something if two of the words were interchanged. Underline these words.

79 You cannot read all that you believe in the newspapers.

80 There are not many winter in the garden in flowers.

81 Week starts a new working Monday.

82 The daughter pushed her mother in a buggy.

83 She went to the town in the afternoon and then read a book all morning.

84 The children enjoyed taking the walk for a long dog.

[85–100]

Imagine you are Lesley Ann James living at 37 Myrtle Cottages, Lower Kindleton, Cheshire, CH4 7BS. Your father was killed in a road accident. Your mother is called Elizabeth Janet and her father's name is Arthur Dawes. She has lived in the same village since she was born and since she was married in 1975 she has worked as a postmistress in the village Post Office. She is not very tall, about 150 cm, has blonde hair and is very pretty, with a good complexion only marred by a mole on her left cheek. She was born on July 27th 1955.

She is very busy looking after the family as well as working and has asked you to fill in this form for her on August 30th 1987.

PART I
TO BE FILLED IN BY ALL APPLICANTS

	Mr.	Mrs.	Miss.	or Title
85 Tick correct box	☐	☐	☐	....

86 Your surname ....

87 Christian names or forenames ....

88 Maiden surname (if applicable) ....

	Married	Single	Widowed	Divorced	Separated
89 Tick correct box	☐	☐	☐	☐	☐

90 Age last birthday .... 91 Country of birth ....

92 Present address ....

....

93 Post Code ....

94 Address where applicant can be reached during the day ....

....

95 Present job/occupation ....

96 Date of birth ....

97 Town of birth ....

98 Height (in metres) ....

99 Visible distinguishing marks ....

....

DECLARATION

I declare that the above facts about me are true

Signature of applicant ....

100 Date ....

[1–6]
Let **a** = 2, **b** = 3, **c** = 4, **d** = 5, **e** = 6 and **f** = 7. Find the value of:

1 **a + c + d + f** .... 2 **f − d + c − a** ....

3 $\dfrac{\mathbf{e \times f}}{\mathbf{b}}$ .... 4 $\dfrac{\mathbf{c \times e}}{\mathbf{b \times c}}$ ....

5 **c × a × d** .... 6 **e⁄a + e⁄b + e⁄a =** ....

[7–11]
Underline the word in brackets which gives the correct answer:

7 **twelve** is to **six** as **twenty** is to (ten, forty, thirty, twelve, four)

8 **eight** is to **twenty-four** as **six** is to (thirty-six, twelve, eighteen, thirty-two)

9 **summer** is to **winter** as **warm** is to (spring, hot, cold, dry, wet)

10 **black** is to **white** as **go** is to (walk, bring, fetch, depart, come)

11 **past** is to **known** as **future** is to (foretell, prophesy, coming, unknown, present)

[12–15]
I live near to the church. The church has a clock which strikes the hours, and also strikes once on the half-hour. One night I awoke and was unable to get back to sleep. I heard the clock strike once, some time later I head its strike once again and later, still awake, I heard a further single stroke.

12 What time was it when I first heard the clock strike? ....

13 What time was it when I heard it the third time? ....

14 How many strokes does the clock strike in twelve hours? ....

15 How many strokes does the clock strike between 1045 and 1205 hours?

....

[16–25]
Underline the word in brackets which is different from any other word in the brackets, yet similar in some way to the three words on the left.

16 Paul   John   James   (uncle, Alan, Jane, Mary, brother)

17 uncle   aunt   nephew   (relation, Henry, Julia, person, cousin)

18 bat   stumps   bails   (cricket, ball, umpire, score, game)

19 lead   zinc   iron   (can, stone, marble, copper, water)

20 second   fourth   third   (one, four, last, first, five)

21 lion   tiger   bear   (rabbit, animal, ostrich, trout, jaguar)

22 sheep   goat   cow   (elephant, giraffe, gazelle, pig, goose)

23 truth   honesty love   (wealth, patience, virtue, cleverness, hatred)

24 seven   nine   eleven   (four, number, ten, series, thirteen)

25 car   lorry   bus   (van, vehicle, train, engine, bulldozer)

[26–33]
In each of the following lines there is a word with mixed up letters. Find what the word should be and put the correct version in the space at the side.

26 All children are fond of tessew and ....

27 spend a great deal of their yemon in ....

28 gynbiu them. Lollipops are always great ....

29 utrovefisa with the youngsters and the shops ....

30 near the shosloc do a roaring trade. ....

31 The fact that sweets are bad for the thete ....

32 does not treed those who are fond of them. ....

33 They eat them just the seam. ....

[34–38]
Complete the series by filling in the blanks:

34 5   8   11   14   ....

35 39   36   32   27   ....

36 AB   CD   EF   ....   IJ   ....

37 A90   ....   D63   E54   F45

38 Ab2   Bc5   Cd8   De11   ....

[39–45]

In each of the sets there are two things which are alike in some way but different from the others. Underline the two things that are similar.

39   colt   horse   cow   elephant   filly   pig

40   airman   shopkeeper   lawyer   soldier   joiner   bus driver

41   England   Scotland   London   Ireland   Edinburgh   Wales

42   kilometre   gram   metre   minute   litre   hectare   penny

43   friendly   mean   kind   generous   happy   stingy   loving

44   lazy   active   still   energetic   noisy   tired   rich

45   beef   cocoa   bread   dinner   coffee   potatoes   cafe

[46–50]

Let $a = 2$, $b = 3$, $c = 4$, $d = 5$, $p = 6$, $t = 7$. Find three letters whose values added together will give you the following numbers, and which will make a recognisable word.

46   9 ....   **47**   12 ....   **48**   15 ....

Now give four different letters which add up in value to give these numbers.

49   22 ....   **50**   18 ....

[51–55]

Fill in the missing word in each line:

51   **sweet** is to **sour** as **commence** is to ....

52   **picture** is to **frame** as **letter** is to ....

53   **today** is to **tomorrow** as **yesterday** is to ....

54   **arrival** is to **departure** as **birth** is to ....

55   **black** is to **white** as **cooked** is to ....

[56–60]

Underline the two words in brackets which go together in the same way as the two words in heavy type.

56   **bricklayer** and **trowel** (wall, bricks, carpenter, saw)

57   **country** and **parliament** (councillor, council, mayor, county, village)

58   **laugh** and **pleasure** (cry, sorrow, joy, fear)

59   **where** and **here** (time, now, again, never, when)

60   **long** and **length** (time, deep, when, height, depth)

[61–65]

Five farmers called Able, Baker, Croft, Daniels and Eager went to market one day. Able, Croft and Eager bought pigs; Baker and Daniels bought sheep; Able and Daniels bought cows; Baker and Croft bought chickens; Able and Croft bought calves and Eager bought a pony for his daughter.

61 Who bought pigs and chickens? ....

62 Who bought cows and calves? ....

63 Who bought sheep and cows? ....

64 I saw a farmer loading a lorry with sheep and chickens. Who was it?

....

65 I noticed one farmer loading a horse-box. What other animals did he have

to transport back to his farm in the Landrover pulling the horse-box?

....

[66–77]

In this passage a word has been left out of every line. The place where the missing word should go is marked with a cross (x). Select the correct word from the list at the end of the passage and write it in at the end of the appropriate line.

66 The bark of a tree is its x. Just as human fingerprints ....

67 differ, so the types and x of the bark vary in different ....

68 trees. The skin of a tree has pores so that the bark can x. ....

69 You can see this by x a piece of cork which is the bark ....

70 of the cork oak. A piece of cork has x of brown running ....

71 through it. These are the x or pores through which air ....

72 is taken in. As a tree grows x its skin grows thicker and ....

73 at the trunk you will find the bark x and forming ridges. ....

74 When you cut x, your skin grows over the wound forming ....

75 a scar. If a sapling or x is broken off from the main tree ....

76 the bark grows over the x. A careful look at a tree will ....

77 x where there used to be branches that have now broken off. ....

channels   cracking   older   yourself   streaks   breathe

patterns   branch   wound   reveal   skin   examining

[78–89]

Here is a list of twelve names which need to be inserted in a telephone directory. Put a number by each name indicating the order in which they will appear in the directory.

78   Mr. R.J. Taylor   (   )

79   Mr. S.G. Taylor   (   )

80   Mr D. Trainor   (   )

81   Mrs. B. Tarbett   (   )

82   Ms. C. Tasker   (   )

83   Mr. C.M. Tasker   (   )

84   Miss L.R. Tamplin   (   )

85   Mr. A. F. Tankard   (   )

86   Mr. V. Tu   (   )

87   Mrs. Dawn Trick   (   )

88   Miss Davina Trick   (   )

89   Mr. David Tranter   (   )

[90–93]

If 1 kg of bacon and two eggs cost £1.38, and 1 kg of bacon and four eggs cost £1.56:

90–91   How much does 1 kg of bacon cost?   ....

92–93   What is the cost of 1 egg?   ....

[94–100]

You are going to visit the Greek island of Paros. The best way is to fly to Athens and take a small local aircraft the rest of the way. You want to go on Thursday 25th September leaving as early as possible in order to get a connecting flight to Paros the same day. Here is a timetable of flights to Athens from London. In these the first day of the week is a Monday.

from LONDON Heathrow local time GMT + 01.00

to ATHINA   local time until 29 Sept GMT + 03.00
   (ATHENS)   local time from 30 Sept GMT + 02.00

Frequency Day No.	Depart–Arrive local times	Flight No.	Dates from – to	
...4567	0945 – 1515	BA560	– 29 Sep	Nonstop
1..45..	0945 – 1415	BA560	30 Sep –	Nonstop
12.4.67	1230 – 1755	OA260	– 29 Sep	Nonstop
12.4.67	1230 – 1655	OA260	30 Sep –	Nonstop
....5.7	1620 – 2145	OA270	– 29 Sep	Nonstop
....5.7	1620 – 2045	OA270	30 Sep –	Nonstop
.2.4...	1620 – 2310	OA264	– 29 Sep	via Rome
.2.4...	1620 – 2210	OA264	30 Sep –	via Rome

94   What time flight would you choose?   ....

95   What is the flight number?   ....

96   Which airport do you leave from?   ....

97   What is the time difference between London and Athens on this date?

    ....

A friend is flying out to join you. She wants to go on Tuesday 30th September.

98   What time flight should she take?   ....

99   What is the flight number?   ....

100   How long is her flight?   ....

[1–4]

1 What letters occur twice in the word **continental** and only once in **countries**?

....

2 What letters occur three times in **continental** and only once in **countries**?

....

3 What letters occur once in **continental** and not at all in **countries**?

....

4 What letters occur once in **countries** and not at all in **continental**?

....

[5–9]

5 I am 5 years younger than Tim. We were both born on 2nd May. Tim was born in 1974. What was my date of birth?

....

6 If I were 7 years older than I am, I would be half as old as my mother, who is 36. How old am I? (17, 18, 11, 10, 12)

7 If I had 75p more I should have twice as much as Jane, who has £1.80, so I must have (£3.60, £2.80, £1.50, £2.95. £2.85).

8 I am the nephew of Mr. Jameson, whose wife is my (mother, grandmother, sister, cousin, aunt).

9 I walked from the school in a north-easterly direction until I came to the church. So the school must be (south, north, north-east, south-west) of the church.

[10–16]
In each set, cross out the word that does not fit in:

10	William	Terry	David	Jason	June	Paul
11	stumps	ball	bails	boundary	bat	
12	referee	forward	striker	back	goalkeeper	
13	bee	wasp	butterfly	moth	spider	
14	tomato	apple	pear	onion	peach	plum
15	spade	hoe	rake	trowel	fork	plane
16	pliers	hammer	spanner	hacksaw	grease	drill

[17–21]

17 If eight is half of seventeen write the letter **X**. If it is not, write the letter **O**.

....

18 If eleven is greater than eight put a ring around the letter **X**, unless eight is greater than nine in which case write the word **No**.   ....

19 Which day of the week contains the greatest number of letters in its name?   ....

20 Write down the middle number between 19 and 25.   ....

21 Take the next even number above 8 from the next odd number below 15.

....

[22–28]
In the brackets at the end of each of the lines write the number of the word that is exactly opposite in meaning to the word on the left.

22	**future**	1 today	2 tomorrow	3 present	4 past	5 forecast	(	)
23	**work**	1 hard	2 laziness	3 play	4 sleep	5 rest	(	)
24	**joy**	1 pain	2 happiness	3 pleasure	4 sorrow	5 tears	(	)
25	**find**	1 reveal	2 hide	3 lose	4 seek	5 reward	(	)
26	**sever**	1 cut	2 strip	3 join	4 slash	5 stick	(	)
27	**bright**	1 shiny	2 glossy	3 dull	4 dismal	5 drab	(	)
28	**lost**	1 missed	2 mislaid	3 found	4 hidden	5 reward	(	)

[29–35]
Look at the diagram and then answer the questions:

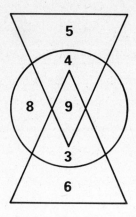

29 What number is in the circle but not in any triangle? ....

30 What number is in the top triangle but not in a circle? ....

31 What number is in the bottom triangle but not in a circle? ....

32 What number is in both triangles and in the circle? ....

33 What numbers are in the bottom triangle and in the circle?

....

34 What numbers are in both a triangle and the circle? ....

35 What number is in a diamond and in the circle? ....

[36–40]
Andrew, Sarah, Carole, David, Carl, Fiona and Gavin are standing
(in that order) in a row facing you. As you look at them:

36 Who is on the left-hand end of the row? ....

37 Who is on the extreme right of the row? ....

38 How many children stand on the left of Carl? ....

39 How many boys stand on the right of Fiona? ....

40 Which person has the same number of children to his right as to his left?

....

[41–45]
Underline the word in brackets which gives the best answer:

41 **stopping** is to **starting** as **coming** is to (entering, leaving, going, departing, staying)

42 **here** is to **there** as **now** is to (soon, then, sometimes, never, tomorrow)

43 **stallion** is to **mare** as **boar** is to (pig, ewe, cow, sow, sheep)

44 **cry** is to **weep** as **complain** is to (enjoy, moan, laugh, shout, grumble)

45 **house** is to **chimney** as **ship** is to (mast, deck, engine, funnel, flag)

[46–47]
Consider these statements and then underline the true statements.

46 John is taller than Richard. William is not as tall as Richard. Therefore: Richard is not as tall as John. William is taller than Richard. Richard is the shortest of the three. Richard is the tallest.

47 The 1030 was a stopping train. The 1030 was late. The 1130 was an express train. It arrived before the 1030. Therefore:
The 1030 was faster than the 1130. The 1130 must have arrived early. The 1130 was a faster train than the 1030.

[48–49]
Consider these statements and write **Yes** opposite true statements.

48 Elephants are larger than bears. Dogs are smaller than bears. Leopards are larger than dogs, but smaller than bears. Therefore:

Leopards are bigger than bears. ....

Bears are not as small as elephants. ....

Elephants are larger than bears. ....

Bears are the largest of all of them. ....

49 I am far away from home. My home was in Leeds. I left it 18 months ago. Therefore:

I live in Leeds. ....

I left Leeds over a year ago. ....

I live just outside Leeds. ....

I am two-and-a-half years older than when I left Leeds.

....

[50–54]

In each set, underline the word that means the opposite of the word on the left.

50	**remote**	distant	far	near	secluded	lonely
51	**simple**	single	complex	silly	signal	difficult
52	**prosper**	flourish	enrich	succeed	thrive	fail
53	**mar**	injure	improve	destroy	build	spoil
54	**grave**	joyful	serious	sedate	friendly	solemn

[55–66]

Here is a passage with one word on each line mis-spelled, although all the right letters are there. Fill in the correctly spelled word at the end of the line.

55 The other force which moves the strawe of the sea ....

56 is the tide. Twice a day, almost every twelve horus, ...

57 the sea reaches its high-water mark and cwite a day ....

58 it retreats to its low-water mark. The grinsi tide is ....

59 called the flood tide and the lafling tide is called ....

60 the ebb. These sangech in level are caused by the ....

61 omon which adds its gravitational pull to that ....

62 of the sun, pulling the great mass of wreat in the ....

63 asse, first in one direction and then the other as ....

64 the thear rotates. Because the earth is rotating and ....

65 the moon vogmin slowly around it, the duration ....

66 of the sedit is prolonged, and they are about 50
minutes later each day. ....

[66–84]

Here is a map of the London Underground. Study it and imagine you have just arrived in London at Euston Station. You are going to stay with a friend who lives near Earls Court. Go by the shortest route and list the stations you will pass or where you will change lines.

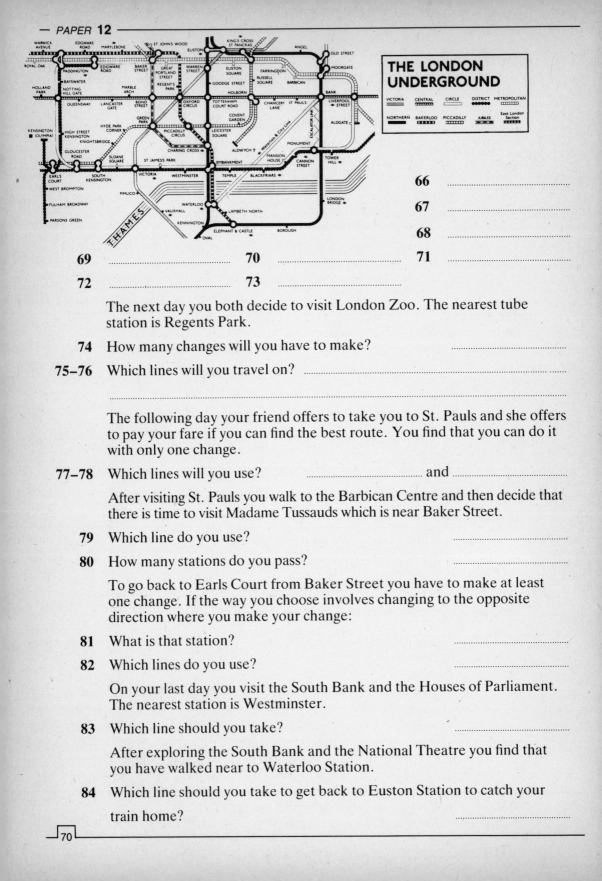

THE LONDON UNDERGROUND

66 ....

67 ....

68 ....

69 .... 70 .... 71 ....

72 73

The next day you both decide to visit London Zoo. The nearest tube station is Regents Park.

74 How many changes will you have to make? ....

75–76 Which lines will you travel on? ....

....

The following day your friend offers to take you to St. Pauls and she offers to pay your fare if you can find the best route. You find that you can do it with only one change.

77–78 Which lines will you use? .... and ....

After visiting St. Pauls you walk to the Barbican Centre and then decide that there is time to visit Madame Tussauds which is near Baker Street.

79 Which line do you use? ....

80 How many stations do you pass? ....

To go back to Earls Court from Baker Street you have to make at least one change. If the way you choose involves changing to the opposite direction where you make your change:

81 What is that station? ....

82 Which lines do you use? ....

On your last day you visit the South Bank and the Houses of Parliament. The nearest station is Westminster.

83 Which line should you take? ....

After exploring the South Bank and the National Theatre you find that you have walked near to Waterloo Station.

84 Which line should you take to get back to Euston Station to catch your

train home? ....

[85–100]
Here is a selection of graphs showing the annual temperature and rainfall in different places in the world. From the descriptions of the places, identify which set of graphs belongs to each place.

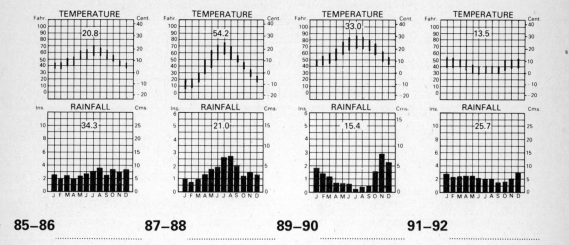

85–86 ....

87–88 ....

89–90 ....

91–92 ....

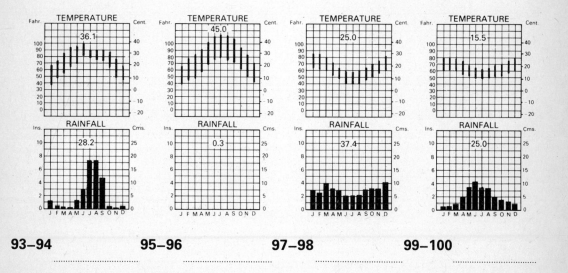

93–94 ....

95–96 ....

97–98 ....

99–100 ....

A. Moscow. This is a northern city a long way inland and so is subject to wide variation of temperatures day and night. It is cold in the winter and relatively warm in the summer. The rainfall is moderate.

B. In Salah. This is an oasis town in the middle of the Sahara Desert. As it is well inland it is out of the moderating effect of the sea and suffers wide fluctuation of temperatures day and night. As it is in a desert, rainfall is very low.

C. Cape Town. This is a coastal city in the southern hemisphere, with modest rainfall, mainly in the winter, and equable temperatures.

D. Manchester. A typical city in the north-west of England. Summer temperatures are relatively low and winters fairly mild. As it is near to the coast of an island the day/night temperatures show only a small fluctuation. Rainfall is fairly high.

E. New Delhi. The capital city of India. It is well inland on a large continental mass with a consequently large fluctuation of daily temperatures. These are high since it is relatively near to the Equator. The most noticeable feature is the rainfall which is very seasonal, occurring mainly during the monsoon.

F. Athens. The capital city of Greece lying on the coast and well south in the Mediterranean Sea. The climate is warm with hot summers and mild winters. Rainfall is low and mainly during the winter months.

G. Port Stanley. The only town on the Falkland Islands. It lies very far to the south and is quite cold, being fairly near the Antarctic. The Falklands are small islands so that the temperature changes are cushioned by the proximity of the sea. Rainfall is fairly constant but not very great.

H. Buenos Aires. The capital city of Argentina. It lies well south of the Equator, and has warm or hot summers and mild winters. It rains regularly throughout the year.

Thomas Nelson and Sons Ltd
Nelson House   Mayfield Road
Walton-on-Thames   Surrey
KT12 5PL   UK

51 York Place
Edinburgh
EH1 3JD   UK

First edition published by Thomas Nelson & Sons Ltd © H H Thomas 1956
This revised edition published by Thomas Nelson & Sons Ltd © A J Thomas 1988

ISBN 0-17-424483-5
NPN 9 8 7 6 5 4 3 2 } Pupils' Book

ISBN 0-17-424484-3
NPN 9 8 7 6 5 4 3 2 1 } Answer Book

Designed, illustrated and photoset by Gecko Limited, Bicester, Oxon

Printed in Great Britain by Ebenezer Baylis & Son Ltd,
Worcester and London